My BIG Book of
MATHS and ENGLISH

AGES 5-7

Written by:
Betty Root
Monica Hughes
Peter Patilla

Helping your child

- Do talk about what's on the page. Let your child know that you are sharing the activities.
- Explain what has to be done on each page, and help with any recording such as colouring and joining up.
- Do not become anxious if your child finds any of the activities too difficult. Young children develop and learn at different rates.
- Let your child do as much or as little as he or she wishes. Do leave a page that seems to be difficult and return to it later.
- It does not matter if your child does some of the pages out of turn.
- The answers to the activities start on page 235.
- Always be encouraging, and give plenty of praise.
- Remember that the gold stars and badges are a reward for effort as well as achievement.

Illustrations by Simon Abbott and Adam Linley

This is a Parragon book
This edition published in 2004

Parragon
Queen Street House
4 Queen Street
BATH, BA1 1HE, UK

ISBN 1-40543-845-2
Printed in Malaysia

Contents

Contents

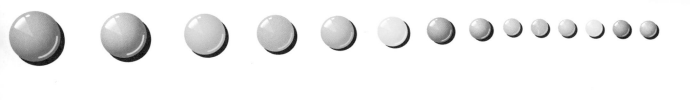

Contents

Contents

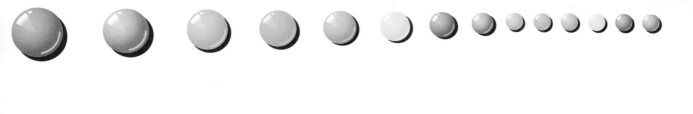

Contents

Read and draw

 Read the sentences and finish the picture.

Draw a tree <u>by</u> the river.

Draw a boat going <u>under</u> the bridge.

Draw a duck <u>on</u> the river.

Draw a car going <u>over</u> the bridge.

Draw yourself climbing <u>up</u> the tree.

Note for parent: This activity helps children to learn positional words such as by, under, on, over and up.

All about me

 Fill in the missing words.

 **My name is** Ana

My age is 67

I live at 67 The Drive

beckenham kent

My school is called st marys

My favourite animal is a snake

My favourite sport is to running

 12

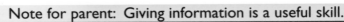 Note for parent: Giving information is a useful skill.

⭐ Draw yourself in the box.
Read the words and draw a line
to the right part.

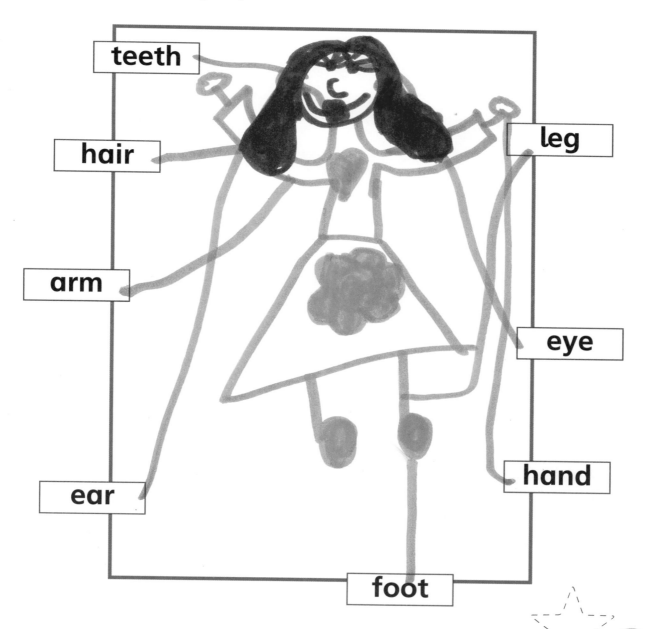

teeth

hair

arm

ear

leg

eye

hand

foot

Note for parent: This activity helps with understanding parts of the body.

13

Numbers for counting

Write the numbers. Join each picture to the right number. Join each word to the right number.

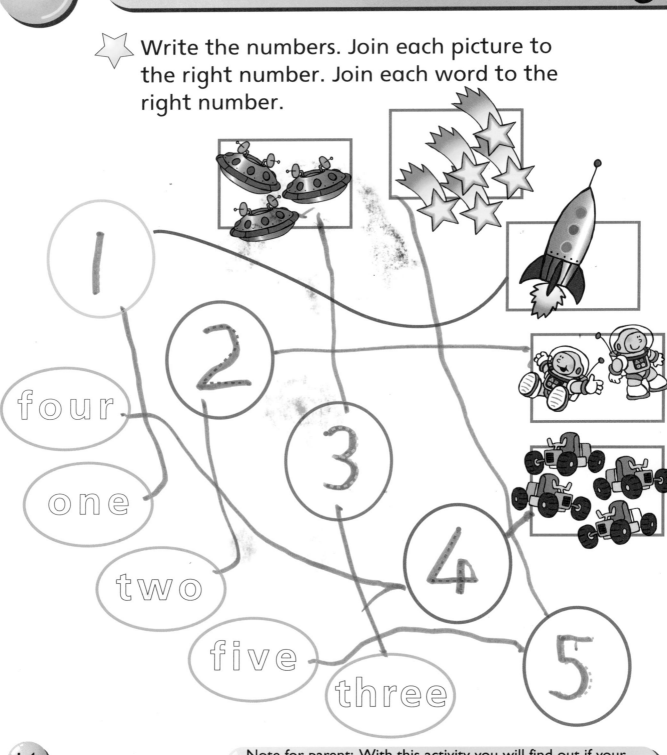

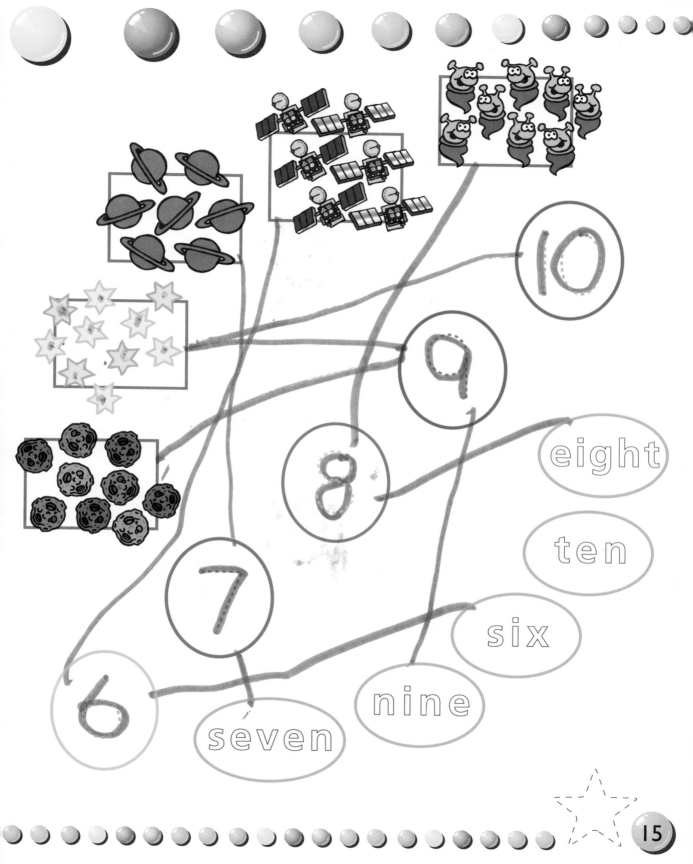

Alphabetical order 1

 Fill in the missing letters and pictures. You can choose your own pictures to draw.

 a

 b *ball*

 c

 d

 e

 f

 g

 *hair* h

 i

 j *jam*

 k

 l

Note for parent: This activity helps children with alphabetical order and beginning sounds.

m — noap.

n

o

p — pen-gwen

q

r

s

t

u

v — lala lala

w — wal-er

x

y

z — zoon

Numbers to 10

 Trace the numbers. Join each kite to the right number. Join each number to the right group of pictures at the bottom of each page.

Note for parent: Ask your child to say each number and word aloud as he or she traces over them.

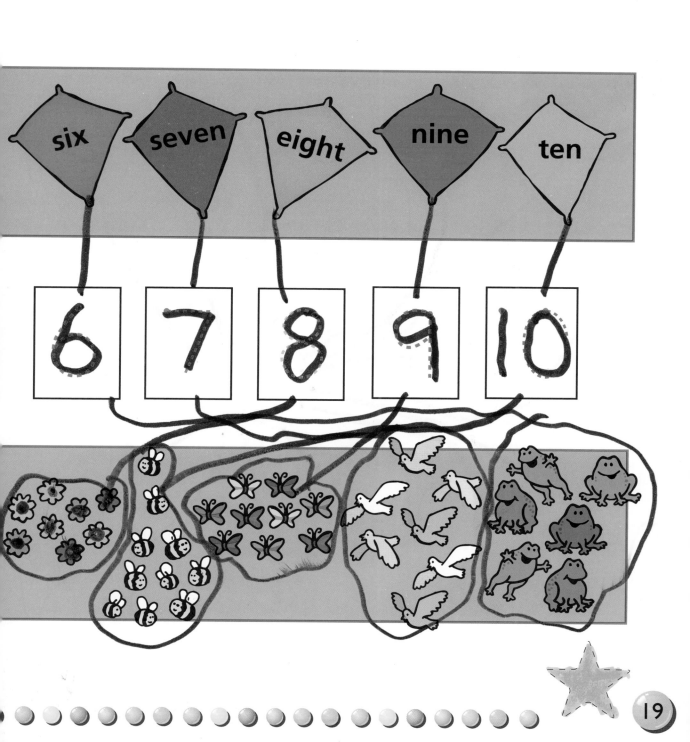

six   seven   eight   nine   ten

6   7   8   9   10

Middle sounds 1

Join the pictures that have the same middle sounds – **a**, **e**, **i**, **o** or **u**.

2+4=6

Note for parent: Children have to listen very carefully to hear middle sounds. Be patient!

Middle vowels

Use the vowels **a**, **e**, **i**, **o** or **u** to complete the words below.

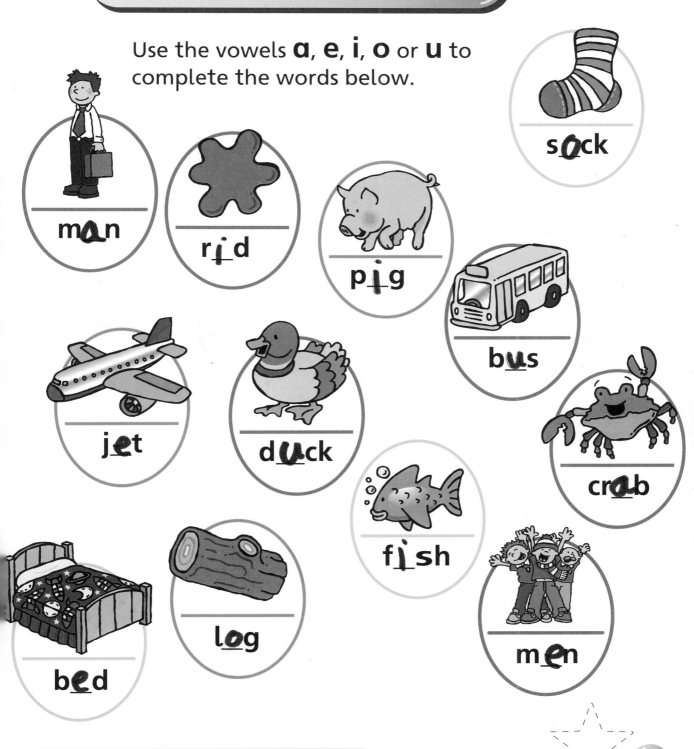

s**o**ck

m**a**n

r**i**d

p**i**g

bus

j**e**t

d**u**ck

cr**a**b

f**i**sh

l**o**g

b**e**d

m**e**n

Note for parent: This activity gives children extra practice in identifying middle sounds.

21

Counting (a)

⭐ Count the spots on each dog. Write the number in the box.

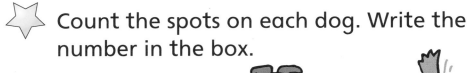

Join the frogs that have the same number of spots.

Note for parent: This activity gives practice in using counting skills in different ways.

Each frog needs 10 spots. Draw in the missing spots.

Join the pairs of dogs. Each pair must have a total of 10 spots.

⭐ Fill in the missing letters.

Note for parent: This activity helps children to
practise alphabetical order without reference.

Searching for words

Read the words in the boxes. Then find them in the big words. Draw a circle around each one you find. The first one has been done for you.

car   too   he   one   ill

or   up   on   she   an

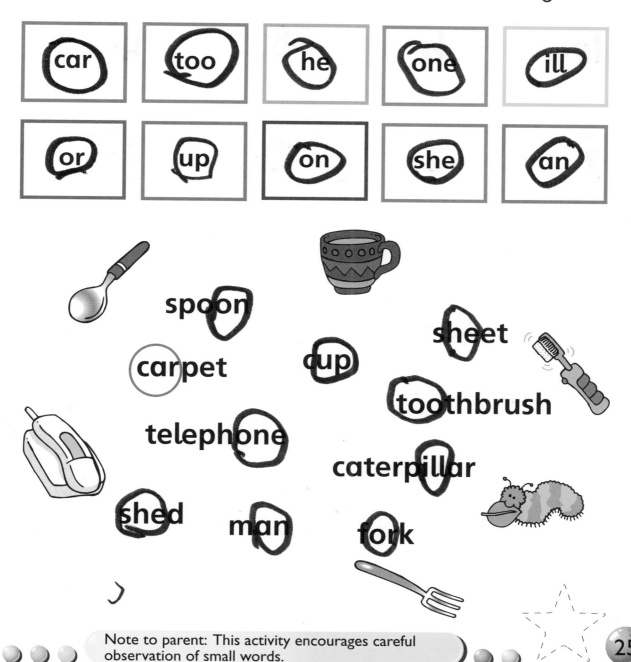

spoon

sheet

carpet

cup

toothbrush

telephone

caterpillar

shed

man

fork

Note to parent: This activity encourages careful observation of small words.

Counting (b)

☆ Count the objects in the big picture. Write the correct number in each box.

| 10 | 🐚 | 6 | 🐟 | 8 | 🦀 | 4 | ⭐ |
| 7 | 🌊 | 9 | 🐟 | 1 | ⚓ | 2 | 🦈 |

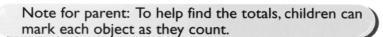

Note for parent: To help find the totals, children can mark each object as they count.

Comparing

 Colour most spaceships red. Colour the rest of the spaceships blue. Write the numbers in the boxes.

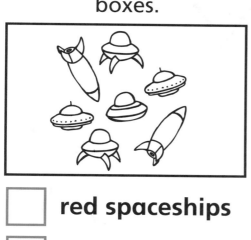

☐ **red spaceships**

☐ **blue spaceships**

☐ **red spaceships**

☐ **blue spaceships**

☐ **red spaceships**

☐ **blue spaceships**

☐ **spaceships altogether**

☐ **red spaceships**

☐ **blue spaceships**

☐ **spaceships altogether**

Note for parent: Your child can choose the number of spaceships to colour red, but there must be more red spaceships than blue ones.

27

Odd one out 1

⭐ Cross out the picture in each row that does not belong.

Note for parent: This activity helps children to classify objects.

Look at the picture. Read the sentences and put a tick next to the ones that are sensible.

The teacher is under the table.

A girl is reading a book. ✔

A boy is painting the door.

The teacher is looking at the children. ✔

A cat is reading a book.

A boy has got a brush. ✔

The hamster is on its cage.

Note for parent: This activity helps children to understand sentences and to make the correct response.

Starting to add

Write in the missing numbers.

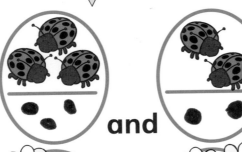 and  make **10** altogether

 and make **12** altogether

 + 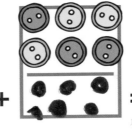 = **14**

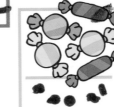 + 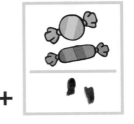 = **12**

 + 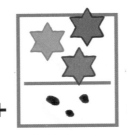 = **14**

 + 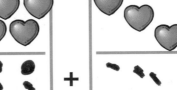 = **12**

Note for parent: In this activity your child is adding pictures, rather than just numbers.

Draw the missing socks above each arrow.

1 + 4 = 5

2 + 3 = 5

3 + 4 = 7

4 + 3 = 7

Write the missing numbers.

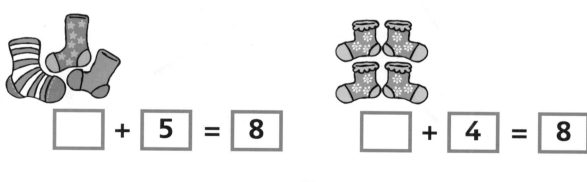

[ ] + 5 = 8

[ ] + 4 = 8

[ ] + 5 = 6

[ ] + 5 = 7

Rhyming pairs

Draw lines to join the pictures that rhyme.

Double beginnings

Choose one of these beginning sounds to complete the words in the boxes.

dr   fl   gr   sp   cl

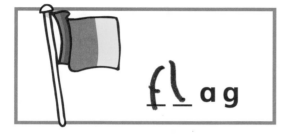

fl ag

c l own

d r agon

sp oon

c l ock

gr apes

fl ower

dr um

Note for parent: This activity helps children to recognize the double beginning sounds dr, fl, gr, sp and cl.

Putting together

 Count each set. Write how many there are altogether.

  **biscuits altogether**

  **cakes altogether**

  **pizzas altogether**

  **ice creams altogether**

  **sweets altogether**

Note for parent: Encourage your child to count on from the first number to find the total.

Count the spots on each monster.
How many spots are there altogether?

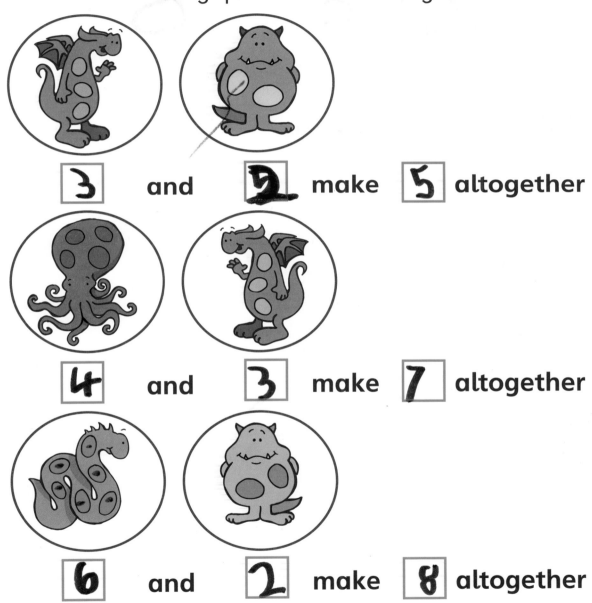

3 and 2 make 5 altogether

4 and 3 make 7 altogether

6 and 2 make 8 altogether

Using labels

 Read these words:

ball ~~boy~~ ~~girl~~ ~~man~~ (car) tree

Now write the words in the boxes below.

car

boy

tree

man

girl

ball

The alphabet

★ Write in the missing letters. Some are capital letters and some are lower-case ones.
Draw your own pictures in the empty squares.

Starting to take away

Dino the Dinosaur eats 2 of everything he sees.
Cross out how many pieces of food Dino eats.
Write how many are left after Dino has eaten.

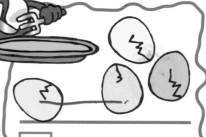

$\boxed{4}$ take away 2
leaves $\boxed{2}$

$\boxed{6}$ take away 2
leaves $\boxed{4}$

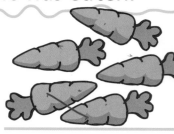

$\boxed{5}$ take away 2
leaves $\boxed{3}$

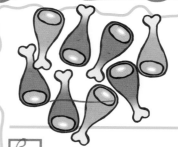

$\boxed{8}$ take away 2
leaves $\boxed{6}$

$\boxed{7}$ take away 2
leaves $\boxed{5}$

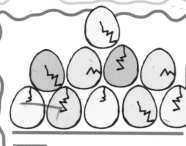

$\boxed{10}$ take away 2
leaves $\boxed{8}$

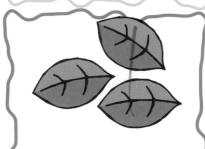

$3 - 2 = \boxed{1}$

$2 - 2 = \boxed{0}$

$9 - 2 = \boxed{7}$

Note for parent: Taking away is the start to learning about subtraction.

How many fish has Charlie Cat eaten from each bowl? Join each START bowl to the correct FINISH bowl.

START

take away 2

take away 1

take away 2

take away 2

take away 3

take away 6

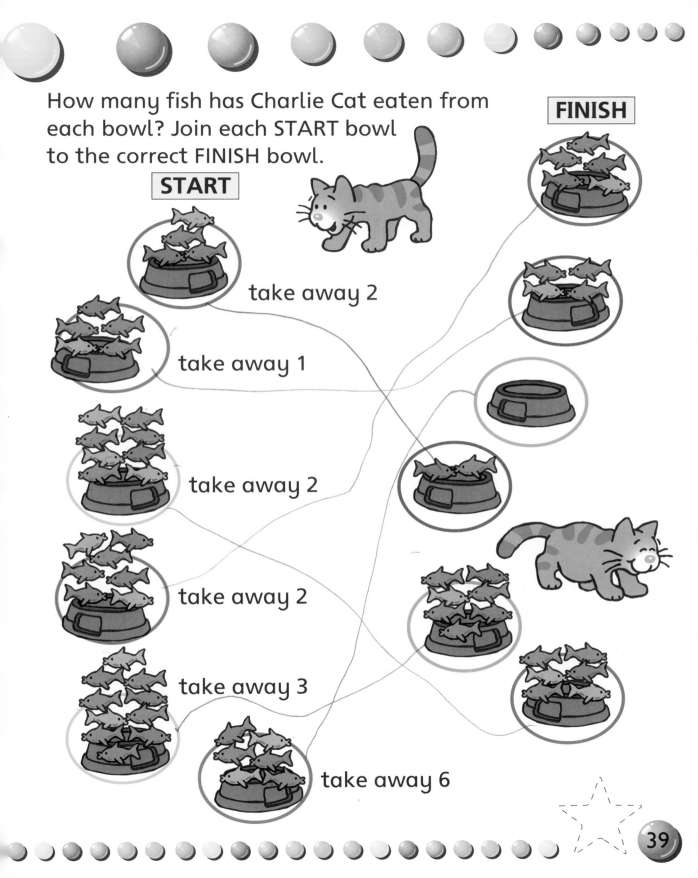

Missing letters n–z

⭐ Fill in the missing letters.

Finding doubles

Find something in the picture that begins with each of the double sounds on this page. Draw a line to join each double sound to the right object.

tr   dr   ch   gl   cl

br   cr   sc   fl   bl

Note for parent: This activity helps children to recognize the double beginning sounds tr, dr, ch, gl, cl, br, cr, sc, fl and bl.

⭐ Cross out two in each set. Write how many are left.

5 take away **2**

leaves 3

6 take away **2**

leaves 4

8 take away **2**

leaves 6

4 take away **2**

leaves 2

⭐ Some birds are flying away. How many are left on the branch?

9 take away **3** leaves 6

Finding differences

 How many more children are there than chairs?

 children

 chairs

difference ➞ 1

7 children

5 chairs

difference ➞ 2

6 children

3 chairs

difference ➞ 3

Note for parent: Finding the difference is the same as counting on from the smaller number to the larger one.

43

Double sounds

 Look at these pictures and say each beginning sound.

 **bl**    **br**    **cl**    **cr**

Fill in the missing letters.

 c l ock    b r idge    c r own   b l ack

Now do the same again.

 **dr**    **fl**    **gr**    **pl**

 g r een    p l ug    d r ill    f l ag

Note for parent: This activity helps children to learn these double beginning sounds: bl, br, cl, cr, dr, fl, gr and pl.

Beginning sounds

⭐ Look at the first picture in each row.
Tick the other pictures in the same row
that start in the same way.

sp ✓ 	Sp ✓ 	Sw ✗ 	Sp ✓ 
st ✓ 	Sn ✗ 	St ✓ 	St ✓ 
sn ✓ 	Sp ✗ 	Sn ✓ 	Sn ✓ 
sw ✓ 	Sw ✓ 	Sw ✓ 	St ✗ 

Note for parent: This activity helps children to learn these double beginning sounds: sp, st, sn and sw.

Looking at shapes

⭐ Some of these foods are whole and some have been cut up into pieces. Join each whole to a cut-up piece.

Note for parent: This activity encourages your child to examine shapes closely.

Matching shapes

Colour the matching shapes.

colour red

colour green

colour blue

colour orange

Note for parent: This activity gives further practice in examining shapes closely.

 Draw a circle around the correct middle sounds.

(a) o
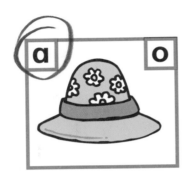

i (u)

(o) a

i (e)

(i) e

a (u)

u (a)

(o) a

(i) a

Note to parent: This activity helps children to choose middle sounds. Some children find this difficult.

Hidden numbers (a)

There are 9 rabbits in each line. Write how many are hidden.

 2

 1

 4

 5

Note for parent: Ask your child to count how many rabbits he or she can see, then count on to 9 to find the difference.

Number machines

⭐ Sweets go into these adding machines. Write
how many come out of each machine.

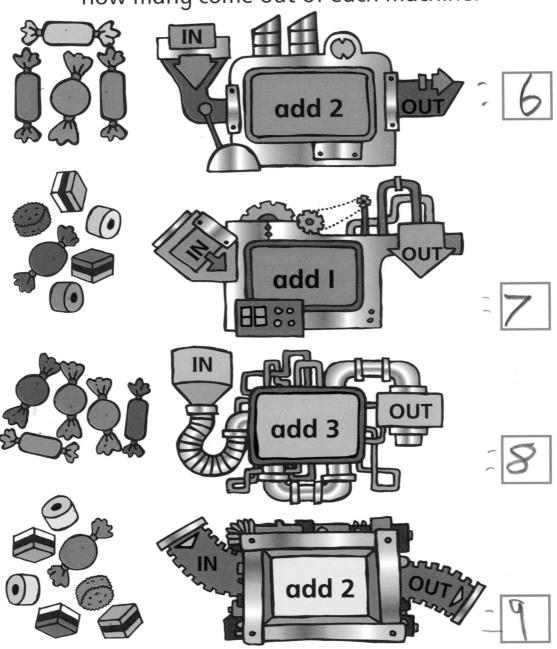

add 2 : 6

add 1 : 7

add 3 : 8

add 2 : 9

Note for parent: Encourage your child to count on from the IN number for
adding. Encourage him or her to count back from the IN number for taking away.

⭐ Drinks go into these take away machines.
Write how many come out of each machine.

= 5

= 2

= 1

= 3

The Enormous Turnip

Look at the pictures. Read the sentences.
Match each sentence to the correct picture.

Everyone fell over and the turnip came out. ___

The farmer saw an enormous turnip. ___

Everyone tried to pull up the turnip. ___

The farmer tried to pull up the turnip. ___

How does it end?

Look at each row of pictures. Tell the story but choose the ending that you like the best.

Note for parent: This activity gives children practice in telling a story from pictures.

53

Solid shapes

⭐ Join each set of shapes to its name.

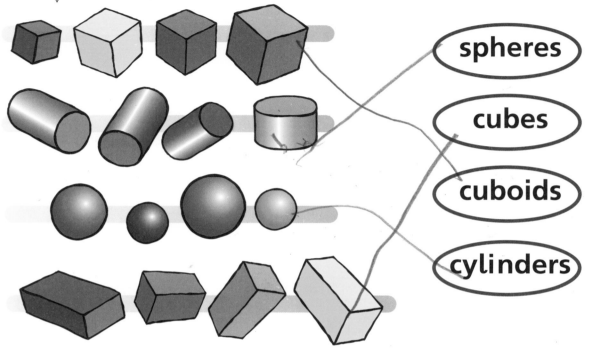

spheres

cubes

cuboids

cylinders

Join the shapes that match.

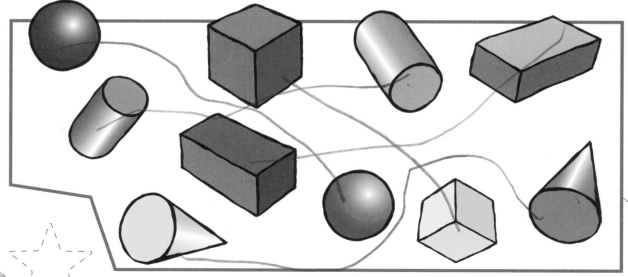

Note for parent: Your child will gradually learn the names of common shapes.

Making lists

⭐ Write the words in the correct lists.

spade

Things I use in the kitchen	Things I use in the garden
spoon, knife pan food processor.	fork spade water-ing can, lawnmo-wer

pan

knife

wheelbarrow

watering can

spoon

frying pan

fork

food processor

lawnmower

55

Making new words 1

 Write the new words you make.

Change the **b** in **bat**  to make c *at*

Change the **f** in **fox**  to make b *ox*

Change the **j** in **jar** to make c *ar*

Change the **d** in **dog** to make l *og*

Now draw a picture of each new word
and write the word in the box.

cat

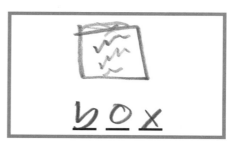

box

car

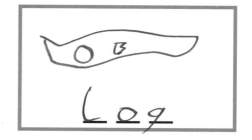

log

Note to parent: Making these new words gives
practice in reading short words.

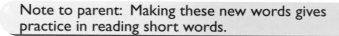

Little words

Find a little word in each big word. Write the little words in the spaces.

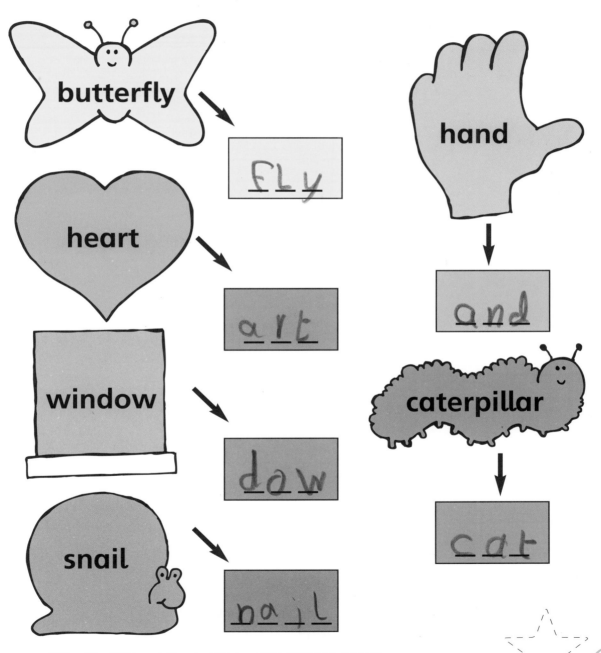

butterfly → fly

heart → art

hand → and

window → daw

snail → nail

caterpillar → cat

Note to parent: This activity helps children to identify words within words.

57

Adding 1

 Draw the extra balloons in each row. Write the correct totals.

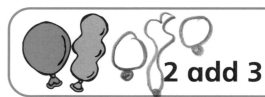

2 add 3

$2 + 3 = \boxed{5}$

3 add 4

$3 + 4 = \boxed{7}$

4 add 5

$4 + 5 = \boxed{9}$

 Write how many there are altogether.

$\boxed{3} \quad + \quad \boxed{5} \quad = \quad \boxed{8}$

$\boxed{4} \quad + \quad \boxed{2} \quad = \quad \boxed{6}$

Note for parent: Make sure your child recognizes the addition sign (+) and the equal sign (=).

 Write how many coloured pencils there are altogether.

$3 + 2 = \boxed{5}$

$2 + 2 = \boxed{8}$

$4 + 3 = \boxed{7}$

$5 + 1 = \boxed{6}$

$6 + 3 = \boxed{9}$

$4 + 5 = \boxed{9}$

 Join each sum to the correct total.

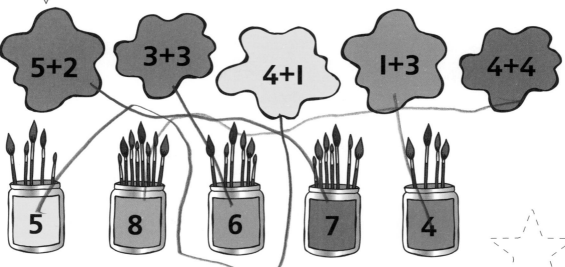

5+2   3+3   4+1   1+3   4+4

5   8   6   7   4

a b c d e f g h i j k l m n o p q r s t u v w x y z

Write the beginning sound of each picture.
Then put the three letters in each row in
alphabetical order.

b	d	C		b d c
h	F	G		f g h
L	m	K		K l m
r	Q	P		p q r
u	S	T		S t u

Little words

Find each little word in one of the big words and then join them with a line.

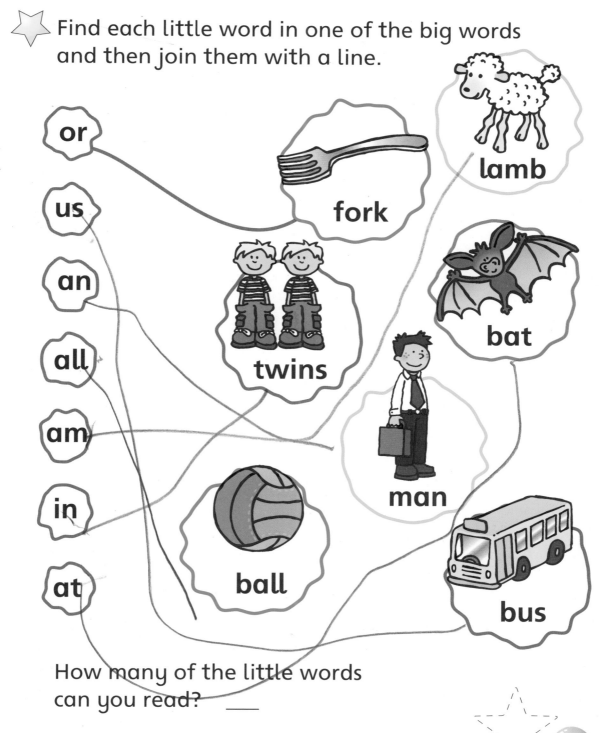

or

us

an

all

am

in

at

fork

twins

ball

lamb

bat

man

bus

How many of the little words can you read? ___

Note for parent: It is great fun to find words inside other words.

61

All about halves

⭐ Colour half of each shape.

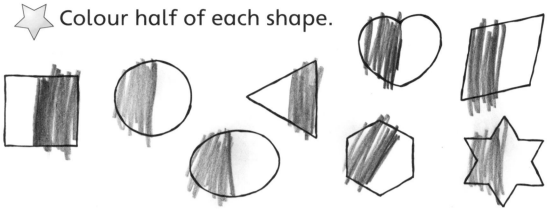

Draw the missing half of each shape.
Join the complete shape to its name.

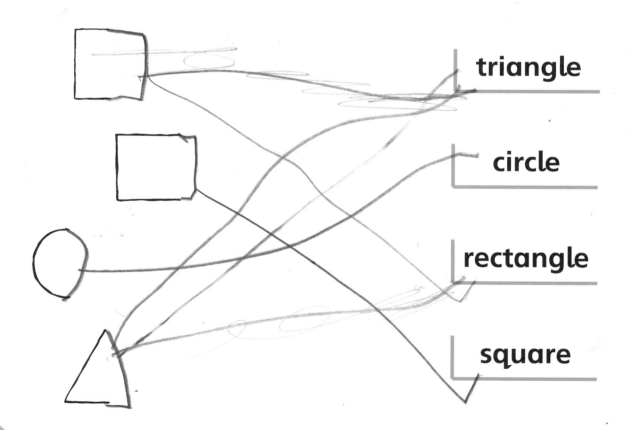

triangle

circle

rectangle

square

Note for parent: Learning about half and fair shares is important in mathematics.

Colour half of the items in each container.

Some marbles are put into two bags.
Put a tick (✔) if the sharing is fair.
Put a cross (✗) if the sharing is not fair.

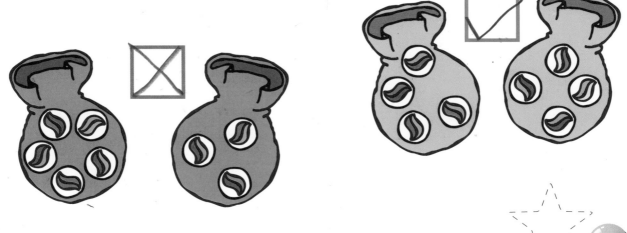

Double doubles

Look at the pictures and say the words.
Draw lines to join two pictures that begin in
the same way.

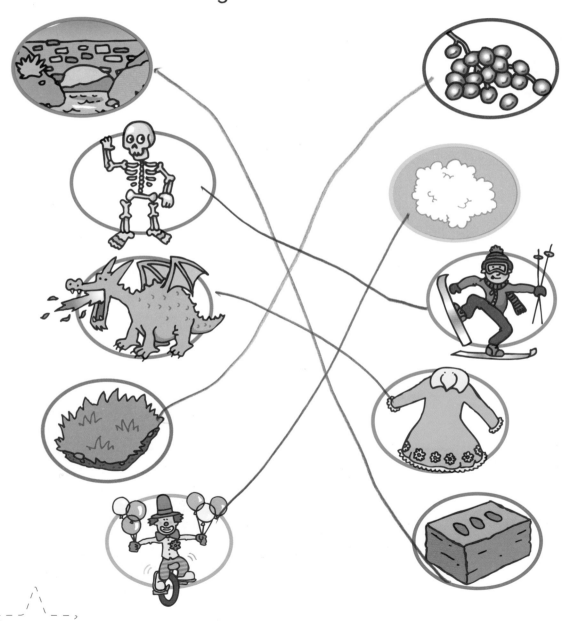

Note to parent: This activity gives further practice with
the double sounds br, sk, dr, gr and cl.

Completing words

 Choose one of these double sounds to complete the words below.

fr sl sp cl tr tw

 c l o c k

 s l i d e

 t r a i n

 s p i d e r

 t w i n s

 f r o g

Note for parent: This activity encourages children to recognize and write the double sounds fr, sl, sp, cl, tr and tw.

Taking away (a)

 Two children get out of each of these trains. How many are left on each train?

7 take away 2 is $\boxed{5}$ **7 − 2 =** $\boxed{5}$

5 take away 2 is $\boxed{3}$ **5 − 2 =** $\boxed{3}$

8 take away 2 is $\boxed{6}$ **8 − 2 =** $\boxed{6}$

 Cross out some flags. Write how many are left.

9 − $\boxed{2}$ **is** $\boxed{7}$

Note for parent: Make sure your child recognizes the subtraction sign (−). Remember to use the words 'subtract' and 'take away'.

⭐ Draw how many balls come out of the machines. Write the totals in the red boxes.

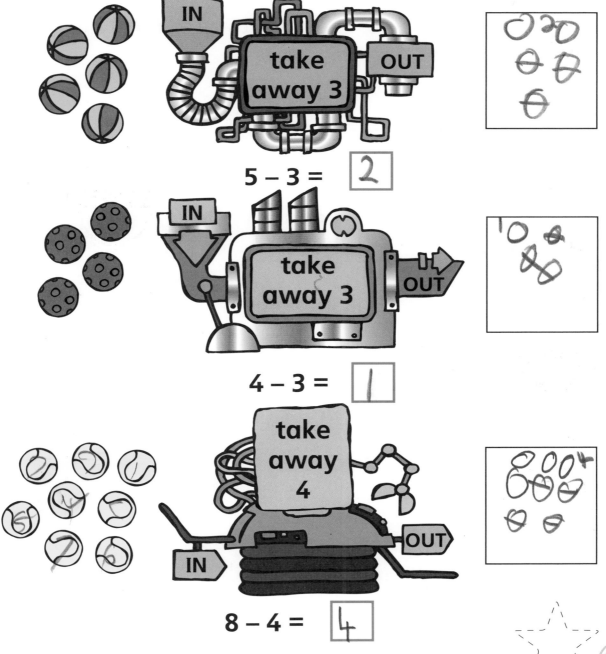

$5 - 3 =$ 2

$4 - 3 =$ 1

$8 - 4 =$ 4

Find the right word

sun ~~bed~~ **boy** **ball** ~~girl~~ ~~tree~~

Choose one of these words to complete each of the sentences.

A little __girl__ put on her dress.

The __sun__ was hot.

I like getting into my __bed__ to go to sleep.

I can see a bird's nest in the __tree__ .

Dad kicked the __ball__ .

A little __boy__ put on his football boots.

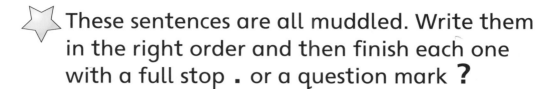 These sentences are all muddled. Write them in the right order and then finish each one with a full stop . or a question mark ?

is time What the

What is the time.

chips I to like eat

I like to eat chips .

do go school When I to

_____

car going The was fast

The car was going fast.

up Who the with went Jill hill

Jill went up the hill with who?

on lap The likes sit to my cat

The cat likes to sit on my lap.

How many capital letters can you count? __5__

Note for parent: This activity gives practice with sorting words to make sense and using full stops and question marks.

Adding 2

 Draw in the extra crayons.
Write the total number of crayons.

1 add 4

$1 + 4 = \underline{5}$

3 add 3

$3 + 3 = \underline{6}$

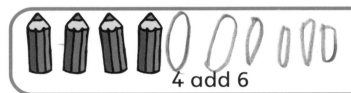

4 add 6

$4 + 6 = \underline{10}$

There should be 10 cherries on each plate.
Draw the missing cherries.

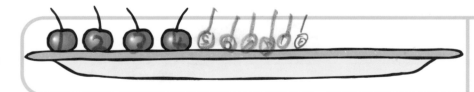

$4 + \underline{6} = 10$

$8 + \underline{2} = 10$

Note for parent: Your child may need to use the number track on page 19 to complete these additions.

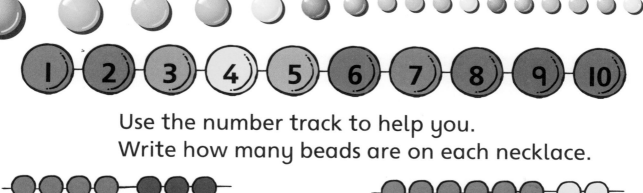

Use the number track to help you.
Write how many beads are on each necklace.

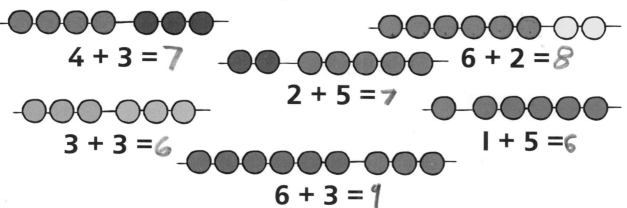

$4 + 3 = 7$

$2 + 5 = 7$

$6 + 2 = 8$

$3 + 3 = 6$

$1 + 5 = 6$

$6 + 3 = 9$

Join the scarves that have the same total.

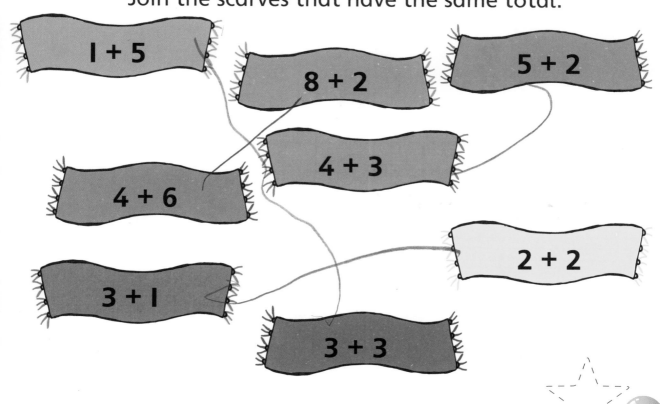

1 + 5

8 + 2

5 + 2

4 + 3

4 + 6

2 + 2

3 + 1

3 + 3

In the right order

Write the beginning sound of each picture. Then put the three letters in each row into alphabetical order. The first row has been done for you.

b	c	a	a b c
f	e	d	f e d
i	h	g	g h i
k	l	j	k l j
n	o	m	n o m

Note for parent: This activity gives practice with placing pictures in alphabetical order.

Crossword puzzle

⭐ Look at the pictures and write the words. The words in the box will help you with your spelling.

globe   bread   ~~frog~~   ~~flag~~   grapes   blue   plug

⭐ Can you think of other words that begin in the same way?

Counting on (a)

Use the number track to count on. Show the jumps and write the answer. The first one has been done for you.

$4 + 2 = \boxed{6}$ | 1 2 3 4 5 6 7 8 9 10

$5 + 3 = \boxed{8}$ | 1 2 3 4 5 6 7 8 9 10

$7 + 2 = \boxed{9}$ | 1 2 3 4 5 6 7 8 9 10

$3 + 4 = \boxed{7}$ | 1 2 3 4 5 6 7 8 9 10

$6 + 4 = \boxed{10}$ | 1 2 3 4 5 6 7 8 9 10

$2 + 3 = \boxed{5}$ | 1 2 3 4 5 6 7 8 9 10

74

Note for parent: These activities will help your child to use a number track or number line to count on to find a total.

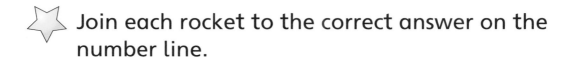

⭐ Join each rocket to the correct answer on the number line.

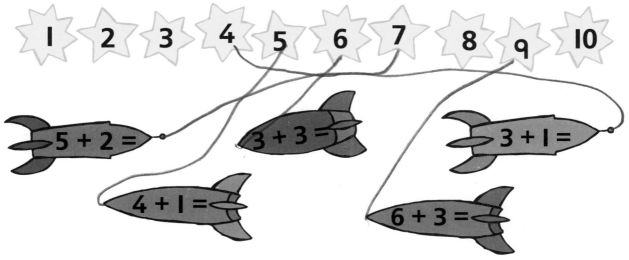

1   2   3   4   5   6   7   8   9   10

5 + 2 =

3 + 3 =

3 + 1 =

4 + 1 =

6 + 3 =

⭐ Write the missing numbers in these counting patterns.

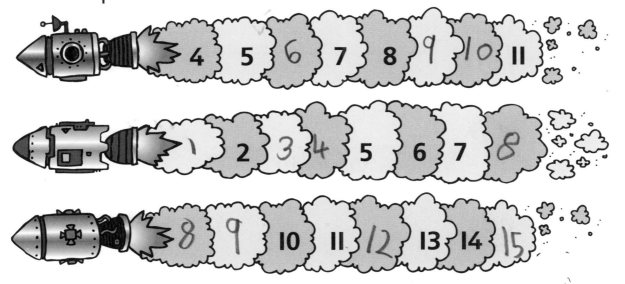

4   5   6   7   8   9   10   11

1   2   3   4   5   6   7   8

8   9   10   11   12   13   14   15

Look at the names and then write them in the register in the correct order. Remember the capital letters.

Alison

Jamilla

Meena

Wendy

Imran

Duncan

Class Register

Alison

Imran

Duncan

Jamilla

Samuel

Meena

Patrick

Wendy

Samuel

Patrick

Where would your name go?

Note for parent: This activity help children to practise using alphabetical order for a familiar situation.

Days of the week

 Look at the pictures.
Read the questions and
then write the correct day.
Remember the capital letters.

Clare

Jack

Monday

On which day does Clare go
trampolining? _wednesday_

On which day does Clare
watch television? _Saturday_

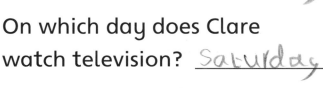

Friday

Tuesday

On which day does Jack go to
the library? _rhursday_

On which day does Clare go
shopping? _Friday_

Saturday

Wednesday

On which day does Jack wash
the car? _sunday_

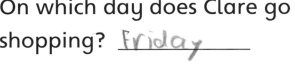

On which day does Clare take
the dog out? _Tuesday_

Sunday

Thursday

On which day does Jack play
football? _Monday_

Note for parent: This activity helps children to learn to read the days of the week.

77

Subtracting

 Cross off the animals to be taken away.
Write how many are left.

4 take away 2

$4 - 2 = $ _2_

7 take away 3

$7 - 3 = $ _4_

8 take away 5

$8 - 5 = $ _3_

Only 3 rockets are needed. Cross off how many
have to be taken away. Write the answer.

$5 - $ _2_ $ = 3$

$7 - $ _4_ $ = 3$

Note for parent: Your child may need to use the number
track on page 21 to complete these subtractions.

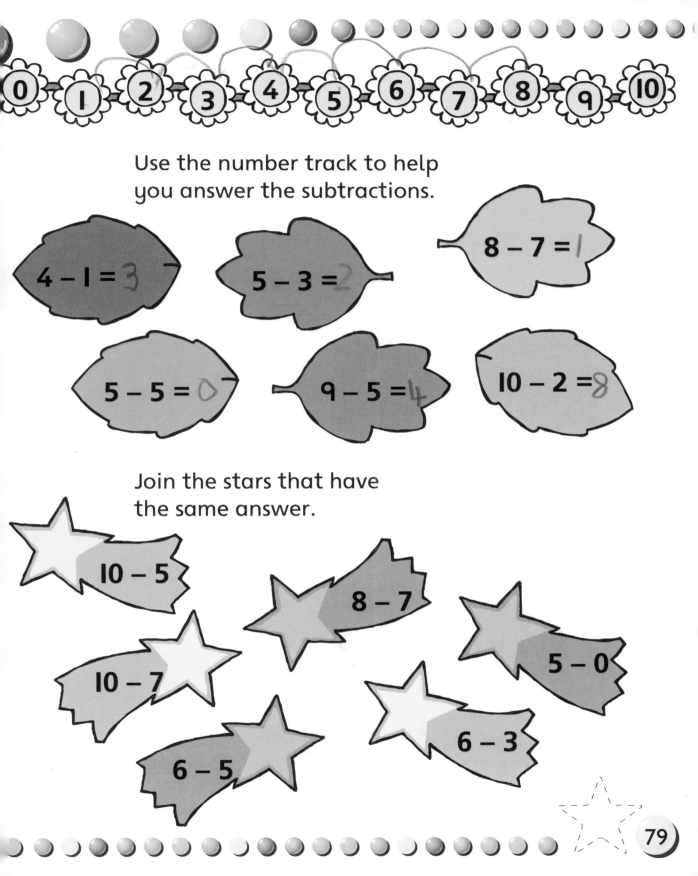

Use the number track to help you answer the subtractions.

$4 - 1 = 3$

$5 - 3 = 2$

$8 - 7 = 1$

$5 - 5 = 0$

$9 - 5 = 4$

$10 - 2 = 8$

Join the stars that have the same answer.

$10 - 5$

$8 - 7$

$5 - 0$

$10 - 7$

$6 - 3$

$6 - 5$

Hidden words

Find a word inside each scarf. Write the words in the spaces.

a n **b u s** h

bus

d e r **p i g**

pig

m q **b e e** x

bee

s **c u p** u r

cup

z o **s o w** b

sow

a o **c a r** c

car

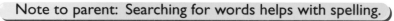

Riddles 1

 Read each riddle and write the answer. You can ask an adult to help you.

The words in the box will help you find the right answer.

| shorts sheep shark shoes ship shell |

1. This sails across the sea. _ship_

2. You find this on a farm. _sheep_

3. You wear these on your feet. _shoes_

4. This fish has very sharp teeth. _shark_

5. You find this on the beach. _shell_

6. You wear these in the summer. _shorts_

Note for parent: This activity helps with understanding and spelling.

Counting back (a)

Use the number line to count back. Show the jumps and write the answer.

6 − 3 = **3**

① 2 ③ ④ 5 ⑥ 7 ⑧ 9 ⑩

5 − 2 = **3**

① 2 ③ ④ 5 ⑥ 7 ⑧ ⑨ ⑩

8 − 4 = **4**

① ② ③ ④ 5 ⑥ 7 ⑧ ⑨ ⑩

9 − 3 = **6**

① ② ③ ④ 5 ⑥ 7 8 ⑨ ⑩

10 − 2 = **8**

① ② ③ ④ 5 ⑥ 7 ⑧ ⑨ ⑩

7 − 6 = **1**

① ② ③ ④ ⑤ ⑥ ⑦ 8 ⑨ ⑩

 82

 Note for parent: Counting back on a number line or number track is a good method for taking away.

Find your way

 Read these instructions. Draw the correct way from the house to the school.

Turn right out of the gate.

Turn right again past some trees.

Walk along the path to the traffic lights.

Cross the road when it is safe.

Turn right and then turn left into **school road.**

Go past the fence and then through the school gate.

Note for parent: This activity helps children to read instructions and follow them.

Telephone numbers

Use this telephone directory to answer the questions at the bottom of the page.

Mr Anderson	9802	Mr Mead	9980
Mr Caswell	9146	Miss Palmer	9544
Mrs Depster	9829	Mr Shah	9827
Miss Heelan	9026	Mrs Todd	9412
Ms Kamara	9530	Ms Walker	9361

What is Mr Shah's number? _9827_

What is Miss Heelan's number? _9026_

What is Mr Caswell's number? _9146_

What is Miss Palmer's number? _9544_

Whose number is 9361? _Ms Walker_

Whose number is 9802? _Mr Anderson_

Whose number is 9412? _Mrs Todd_

Whose number is 9829? _Mrs Depster_

Do you know your own telephone number at home?

0208650 3829

85

Flat shapes

 Cross the odd one out in each box.

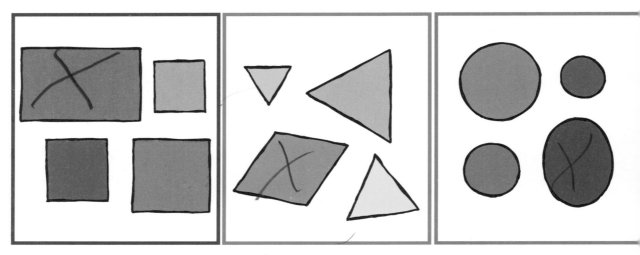

Tick all the shapes that are the same in each row.

Note for parent: This activity gives practice in recognizing shapes.

Sets and pairs

Join each set of shapes to its name.

triangles

circles

rectangles

squares

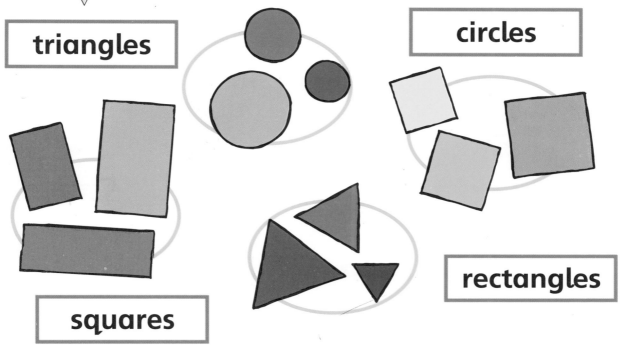

Join the shapes that match.

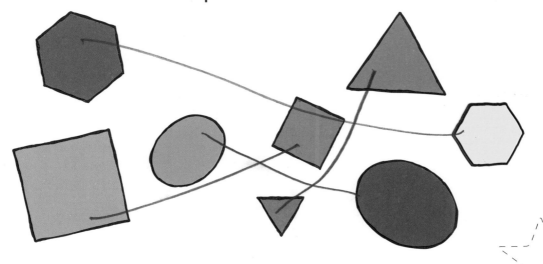

Note for parent: Gradually your child should learn the names of common shapes.

Last letters

Say the name of each picture. Tick the correct ending letter.

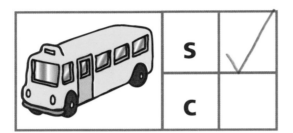

s	✓
c	

g	✓
p	

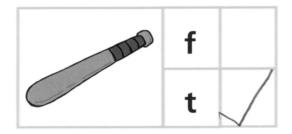

f	
t	✓

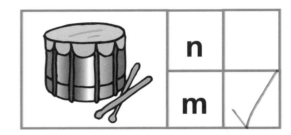

n	
m	✓

b	✓
d	

c	
k	✓

g	✓
p	

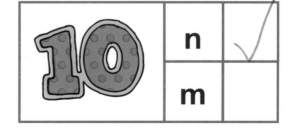

n	✓
m	

Note to parent: Children need to listen carefully to identify last letters.

Matching pairs

Look at the picture. Can you find all the things listed below? Tick each box as you find them.

Find two things that begin with **ch**. ☑ ☑

Find two things that begin with **tr**. ☑ ☑

Find two things that begin with **str**. ☑ ☑

Find two things that begin with **sw**. ☑ ☑

Find two things that begin with **dr**. ☑ ☑

Find two things that begin with **cr**. ☑ ☑

Note for parent: This activity helps children to identify double sounds by both pictures and letters.

Addition bonds (a)

⭐ Make these totals in different ways. Write the answers in the boxes.

6

0 + 6
1 + 5
2 + 4

8

1 + 5 8
2 + 4
3 + 2

9

1 + 5 9
2 + 4 8
3 + 3 7

7

0 + 8
1 + 5
2 + 4

Note for parent: Addition bonds are all the different ways that a total can be made with two numbers. Remind your child that, for example, 4 + 5 gives the same answer as 5 + 4.

⭐ Draw a line from each flower to the pot with the correct total.

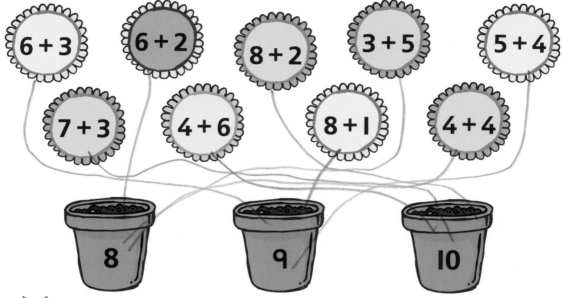

6 + 3   6 + 2   8 + 2   3 + 5   5 + 4

7 + 3   4 + 6   8 + 1   4 + 4

8   9   10

⭐ What can you see if you colour all the shapes with a total of 10?

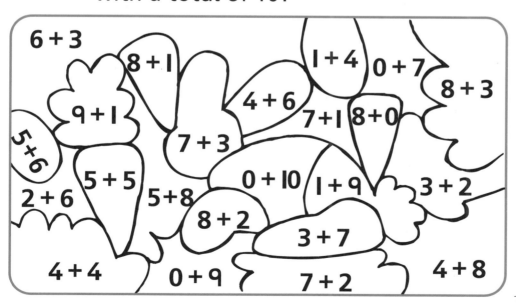

6 + 3
8 + 1
1 + 4   0 + 7
8 + 3
4 + 6
9 + 1   7 + 1   8 + 0
7 + 3
5+6
5 + 5   0 + 10   1 + 9   3 + 2
2 + 6   5+8
8 + 2
3 + 7
4 + 4   0 + 9   7 + 2   4 + 8

Match each word to the correct meaning.
Draw a line to join them.

elephant

A large animal that can
jump very well. It carries its
young in a pouch. It comes
from Australia.

kangaroo

A small animal with long
arms and feet that it uses
like hands. It lives in
jungles.

monkey

A large animal with a long
trunk and ivory tusks. It
lives in Africa and Asia.

panda

An animal like a horse with
black and white stripes. It
lives in Africa.

zebra

A black and white animal
like a bear. It lives in China.

Reading an index

 Use the index below to answer the questions at the bottom of the page.

Index

Apes	10	Kangaroos	20
Bears	8	Monkeys	6
Chimpanzees	14	Penguins	28
Crocodiles	22	Sharks	4
Dolphins	26	Turtles	12
Giraffes	18	Whales	16

Page 18 is about _____

Page 28 is about _____

Page 16 is about _____

Page 8 is about _____

Page 12 is about _____

Apes are on page _____

Sharks are on page _____

Kangaroos are on page _____

Giraffes are on page _____

Chimpanzees are on page _____

Which page would you like to read? ____

Why? _____

Time (a)

Write the missing numbers on the clock.

Write the times under each clock.

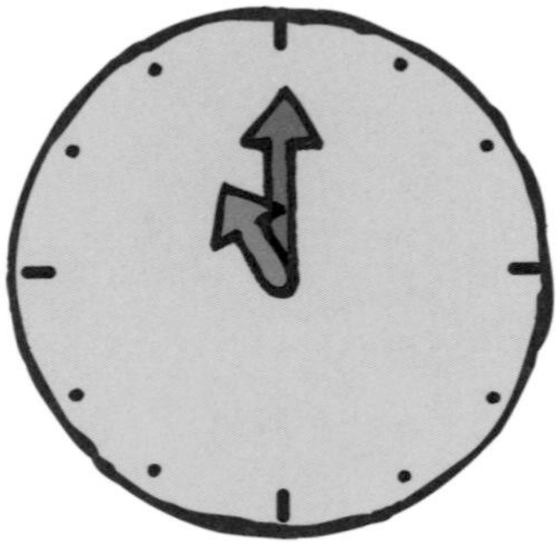

11 o'clock

8 o'clock

5 o'clock

Note for parent: This activity will help your child to start recognizing simple times

Look at the times. Draw in the missing hands.

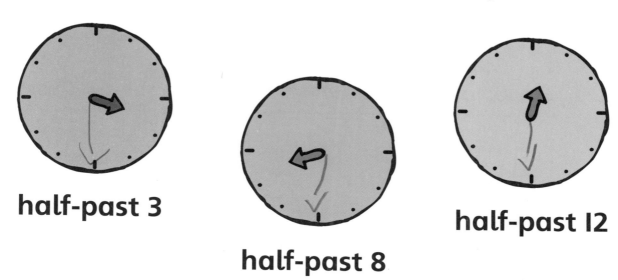

half-past 3

half-past 8

half-past 12

Write the times under each clock.

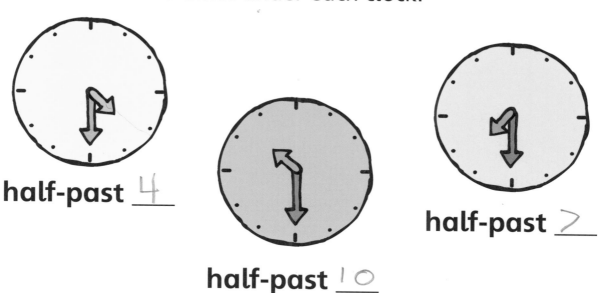

half-past 4

half-past 10

half-past 2

Find the animal

Colour in brown all the words beginning with **br**.
Colour in red all the words beginning with **dr**.
Colour in yellow all the words beginning with **st**.
Colour in green all the words beginning with **gl**.
Colour in blue all the words beginning with **sk**.

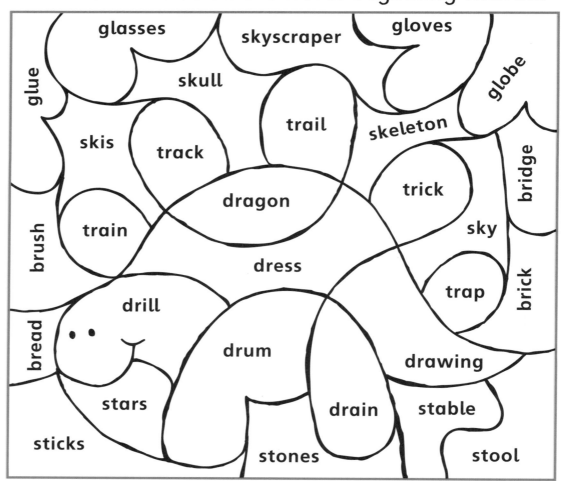

Which animal can you see?

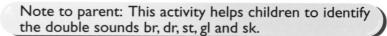

Note to parent: This activity helps children to identify
the double sounds br, dr, st, gl and sk.

More than one

 You add the letter **s** when there is more than one. Write the whole words in the spaces.

 duck  _ _ _ _ _

 pig  _ _ _ _

 cow  _ _ _ _

 farmer  _ _ _ _ _ _ _

 cat  _ _ _ _

Note for parent: This activity helps children to learn about plurals.

97

Addition facts

⭐ Write the answers in the boxes. Use the number track to help you.

$4 + 3 = \boxed{}$ $6 + 2 = \boxed{}$ $5 + 5 = \boxed{}$

$9 + 1 = \boxed{}$ $7 + 2 = \boxed{}$ $3 + 5 = \boxed{}$

$2 + 4 = \boxed{}$ $4 + 4 = \boxed{}$ $6 + 3 = \boxed{}$

⭐ The top can is the total of the two cans below. Write the missing numbers. The first one has been done for you.

⭐ Write the missing numbers.

🍬 + 3 = 7   🍬 + 2 = 5   4 + 🍬 = 9

6 + 🍬 = 9   🍬 + 8 = 10   5 + 🍬 = 8

🍬 + 2 = 8   3 + 🍬 = 6   🍬 + 7 = 10

⭐ Follow these trails to reach 10. Write the missing totals.

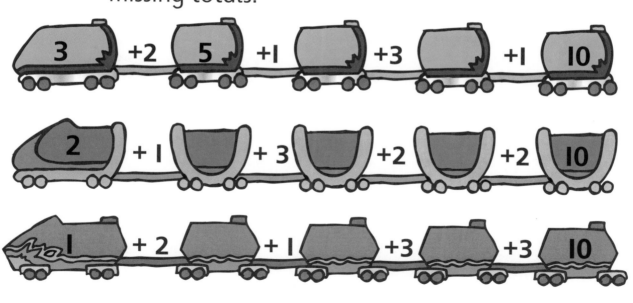

Patterns in words

Make two more words by adding one letter.

b<u>all</u>　　**＿all**　　**＿all**

Write a sentence with each of the two words you have made.

1. _____

2. _____

Now do the same again.

m<u>an</u>　　**＿an**　　**＿an**

h<u>at</u>　　**＿at**　　**＿at**

1. _____

2. _____

1. _____

2. _____

Note for parent: This activity encourages children to look for patterns in words.

Find the rhymes

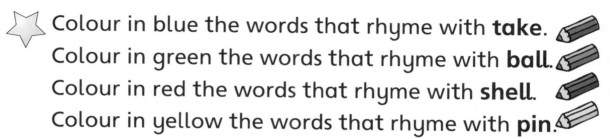

Colour in blue the words that rhyme with **take**.

Colour in green the words that rhyme with **ball**.

Colour in red the words that rhyme with **shell**.

Colour in yellow the words that rhyme with **pin**.

out   no   me   but

spin   bed

is

up   small   go

of   bin

tall

if   fin   on

lake   call   bake

dog   tin   my

you   fall   bad

girl   bell   fell

boy

it

wish   well   sell   cat

Note for parent: This activity helps children to
see patterns and to hear rhymes in words.

101

Counting to 20

⭐ Write in the missing numbers.

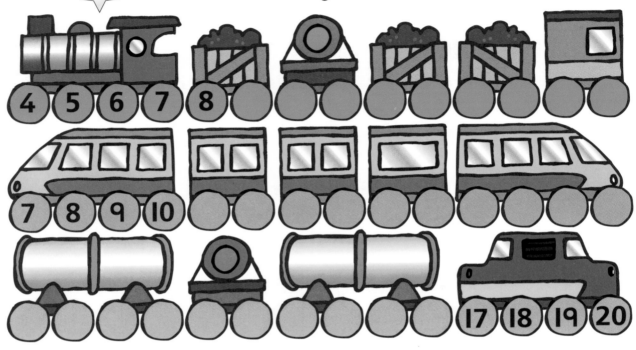

Join each word to a number.

12	eleven	twenty	16
15	fourteen	sixteen	20
11	twelve	thirteen	17
14	fifteen	seventeen	13

Note for parent: This activity gives your child practice in counting to 20, and in recognizing numbers and words.

Join the dots

Join the dots in order.
Can you name the mystery animals?

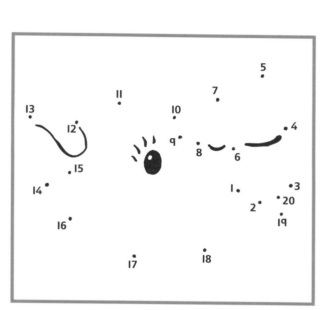

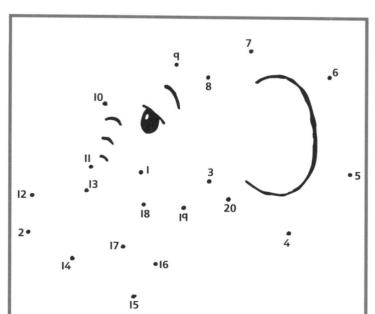

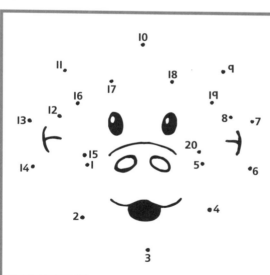

Note for parent: This activity gives further practice in counting up to 20.

Make a word

 Draw a line to join two parts together to make a word.

str	ack
tr	asses
gl	erries
bl	ain
ch	ew
scr	ing

 Write the words beside the correct pictures.

 _ _ _ _ _ _

 _ _ _ _ _

_ _ _ _ _ _ _

 _ _ _ _ _

 _ _ _ _ _ _ _ _

 _ _ _ _ _

Note for parent: Building words with picture clues is an important skill.

Same endings

 Join the pictures that end in the same way.

_ _

_ _

_ _

_ _

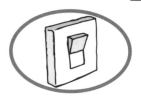

_ _

_ _

 Write the last two letters of each word in the spaces. The letters in the box will help you.

ck sh ch ce ar

Subtraction facts

 Write the answers in the boxes. Use the number track to help you.

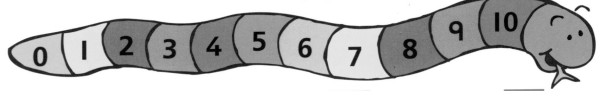

6 − 4 = ☐   7 − 3 = ☐   5 − 1 = ☐

8 − 5 = ☐   6 − 3 = ☐   9 − 4 = ☐

10 − 5 = ☐   7 − 4 = ☐   8 − 3 = ☐

 Colour the squares that have an answer of 4. What can you see?

6 − 1	5 − 1	7 − 2	7 − 4	8 − 2	8 − 3
5 − 2	7 − 3	6 − 3	10 − 1	9 − 7	5 − 4
3 − 2	10 − 6	8 − 5	4 − 4	6 − 4	10 − 5
10 − 7	4 − 0	9 − 6	9 − 5	5 − 0	6 − 5
8 − 3	8 − 4	6 − 2	5 − 1	7 − 3	4 − 4
5 − 3	9 − 4	7 − 1	10 − 6	8 − 6	3 − 0

Note for parent: These activities give practice in learning the subtraction facts within 10.

⭐ Write the missing numbers.

⬡ − 4 = 3   △ − 2 = 4   ⬤ − 3 = 2

8 − ⬡ = 4   6 − ⯃ = 3   7 − ◻ = 5

▭ − 6 = 3   ⬯ − 5 = 4   10 − ✦ = 6

⭐ Draw a line to join each pair of stars with the same answer.

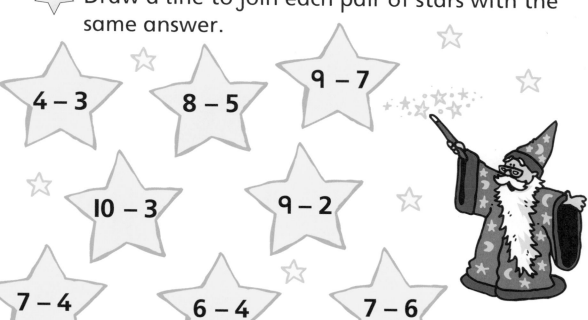

4 − 3   8 − 5   9 − 7

10 − 3   9 − 2

7 − 4   6 − 4   7 − 6

Adding the letter e

 Add the letter **e** to the end of each word to make a new word. Write the new word and draw a picture of it.

cub _ _ _ _ _

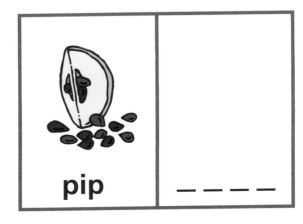

pip _ _ _ _ _

fir _ _ _ _ _

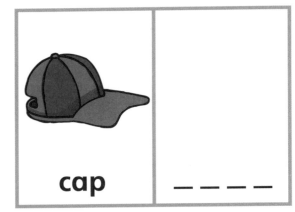

cap _ _ _ _ _

Note for parent: This activity helps children to understand silent 'e'.

Making sets

⭐ Some words go together to make sets. Read the words and write them in the correct set.

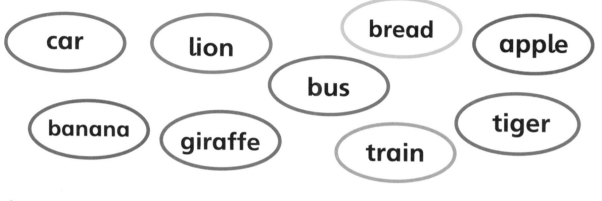

car   lion   bread   apple

bus

banana   giraffe   tiger   train

transport

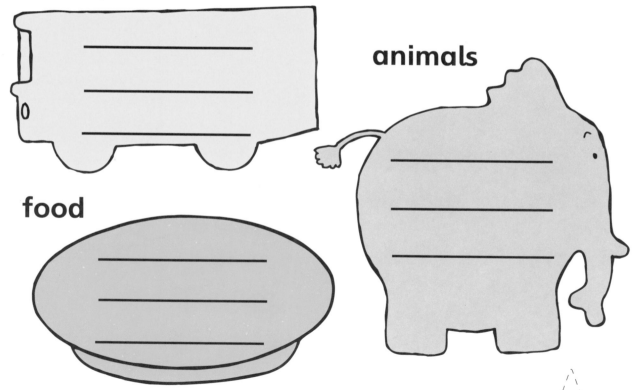

animals

food

Note for parent: This activity encourages children to read words carefully in order to classify them.

109

⭐ Use the number line to help you count on. Join each monster to its correct answer on the line.

8 + 3

9 + 5

8 + 7

6 + 7

9 + 9

6 + 4

0 1 2 3 4 5 6 7 8 9 10 11 12 13 14 15 16 17 18 19 20

10 + 3

10 + 5

10 + 8

10 + 6

10 + 10

10 + 1

Note for parent: This activity will help your child to use a number line to count on and back.

Use the number line to help you count back. Join each spaceship to its correct answer on the line.

12 – 8

12 – 6

13 – 4

11 – 9

16 – 8

12 – 5

0 1 2 3 4 5 6 7 8 9 10 11 12 13 14 15 16 17 18 19 20

20 – 4

20 – 5

20 – 6

20 – 7

20 – 8

20 – 2

Measuring

 Draw a longer worm.

Draw a bigger flower.

Draw a taller rocket.

Draw a shorter lamp post.

Join up the pictures in order of size.
Start with the smallest.

Sorting

⭐ Draw each picture in the correct box.

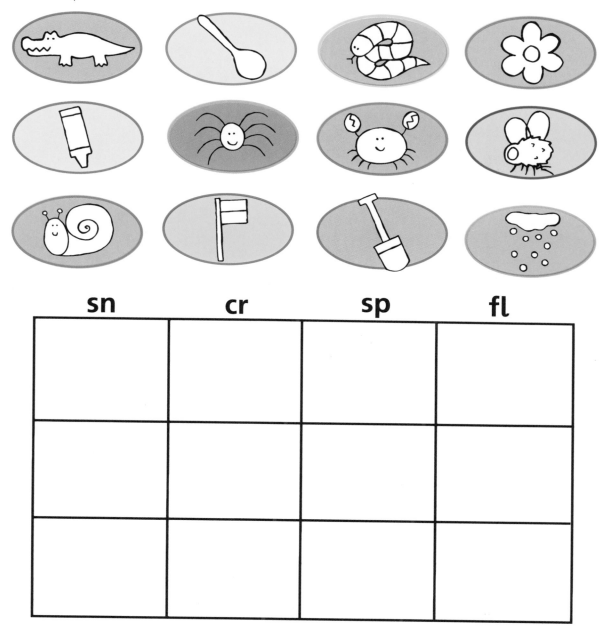

sn	cr	sp	fl

Note to parent: This activity encourages children to classify by beginning sounds.

Number words

 Colour the balloons.

1 = red   2 = purple   3 = yellow   4 = blue

5 = green   6 = red   7 = purple

8 = yellow   9 = blue   10 = green

one

two

three

four

five

six

seven

eight

nine

ten

Note to parent: Learning to recognize written numbers is an important skill.

Word endings 1

Look at the first picture in each row.
Draw a ring round two pictures in each row
that have the same ending as the first.

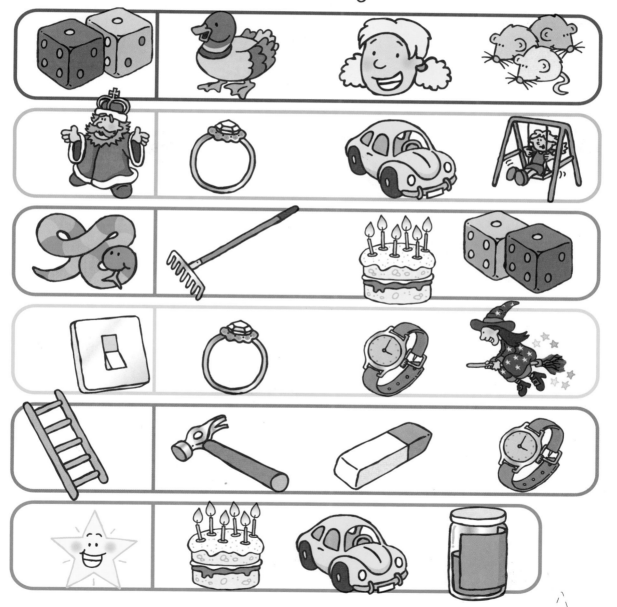

Note to parent: This activity encourages
children to listen carefully to word endings.

115

Adding to 12

Write the totals.

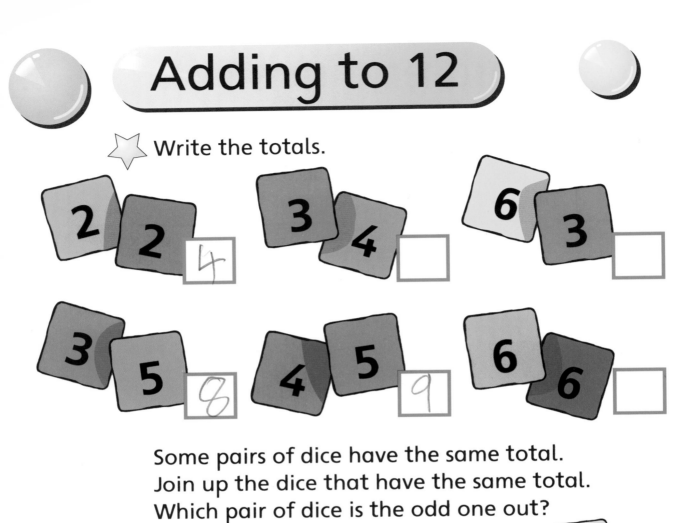

2 2 4

3 4 ☐

6 3 ☐

3 5 8

4 5 9

6 6 ☐

Some pairs of dice have the same total.
Join up the dice that have the same total.
Which pair of dice is the odd one out?

5 5

6 5

6 4

3 1

2 2

5 2

5 4

6 1

6 3

 Write the missing number in each box.

3 + 5 = 8

2 + 8 = 10

☐ + 7 = 12

7 + ☐ = 11

☐ + 5 = 9

Here is a pair of number adding machines.
Write in the missing numbers.

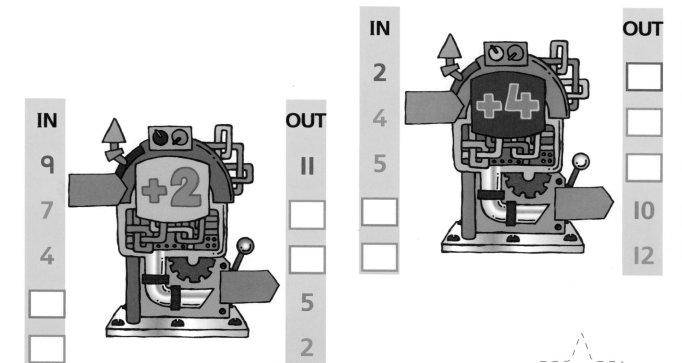

IN
9
7
4
☐
☐

+2

OUT
11
☐
☐
5
2

IN
2
4
5
☐
☐

+4

OUT
☐
☐
☐
10
12

Word endings 2

 Look at the first picture in each row. Draw a ring around another picture in the row that has the same ending.

  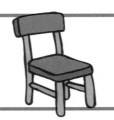 

Note for parent: This activity helps children to recognize the endings ll, ck, ing and er.

⭐ Read the sentences and write your answers in the spaces. The pictures will help you.

You get water from this.

_ _ l l

You put your key into this.

_ _ c k

He wears a crown on his head.

_ _ n g

You put this in a post box.

_ _ _ _ e r

Subtraction bonds 1

Find different ways of making 3 and 4.

3

4 – 1
7 –
3 –
9 –
8 –

4

7 –
5 –
9 –
8 –
6 –

Find different ways to make the answer of 5 .

Note for parent: These activities will help your child

Adding to 20 (a)

The totals on the astronauts match the spaceships. Write in the missing numbers.

Some spaceships have even answers.
Colour them red.

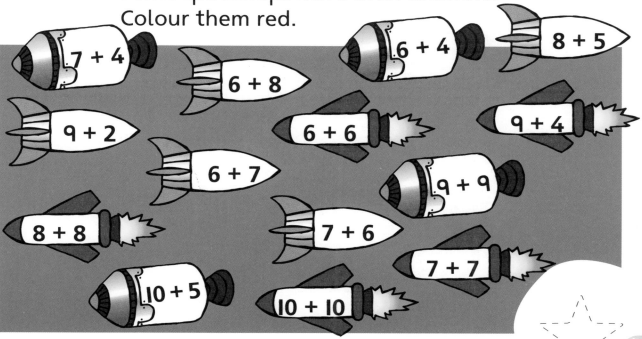

Making totals

 Count each set. Write the totals.

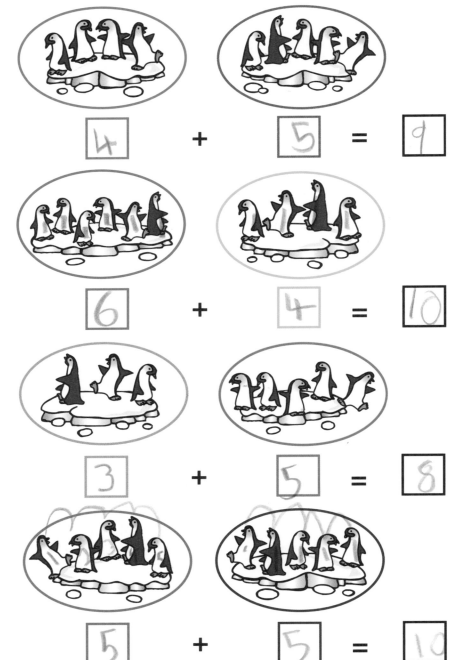

4 + 5 = 9

6 + 4 = 10

3 + 5 = 8

5 + 5 = 10

Note for parent: This activity gives your child

 Draw snowflakes to make the totals.

  $6 + \boxed{4} = 10$

  $5 + \boxed{7} = 12$

  $\boxed{7} + 3 = 10$

 Join pairs of numbers that total 12.

All about nouns

 Words that name people, animals, things and places are called nouns. Read these sentences and draw a line under each noun.

The boy is reading a book.

The girl is looking at the television.

The dog is playing with a ball.

The man is cutting the grass.

Find another noun in each picture and write it below.

_____   _____

_____   _____

Note to parent: This activity helps children to learn about nouns.

An adjective tells you more about someone or something.
Choose an adjective to fill in the missing words in the sentences below.

cold　　**windy** ✓　　**blue** ✓
happy　　**small** ✓　　**fresh** ✓

1. A ladybird is very _Small_.

2. The leaves fell off the tree because it was _windy._

3. The sun was shining and the sky was _blue_.

4. Dad had just picked the flowers so they were _fresh_.

5. The dog was _happy_ because he had a new ball.

6. It was _cold_ in the garden and there was ice on the pond.

Subtracting to 12

⭐ Write the answers at the end of the trail.

Each child only catches fish to match the number on his or her vest.

Join up each child to the correct fish.

Colour the fish that no one catches.

Note for parent: Encourage children to work the answers out quickly and not rely on their fingers.

⭐ Write the missing numbers.

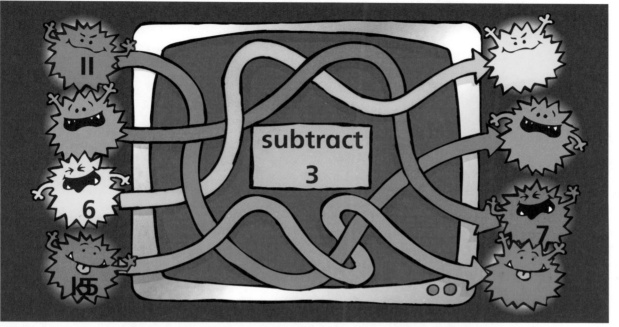

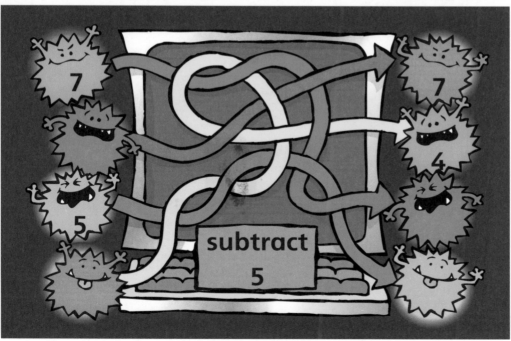

Note for parent: This activity gives further practice in subtracting up to 12.

Learning about **ar**

 Complete each word with the letters **ar**.
Draw a picture in each box.

 c a r

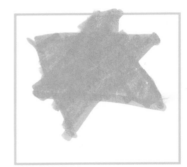 s t _a r_

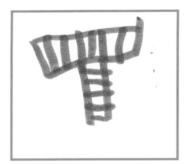 s c _a r_ f

 b _e_ _e_ n

s h _i_ _l_ k

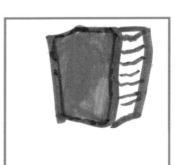 c _a r_ d

Note for parent: This activity helps children to practise the sound ar, and to read words.

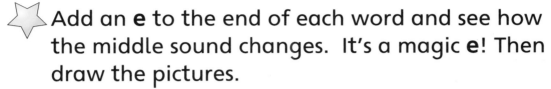

⭐ Add an **e** to the end of each word and see how the middle sound changes. It's a magic **e**! Then draw the pictures.

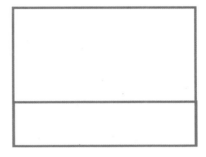

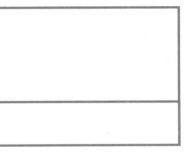

⭐ Can you think of a word that rhymes with each of the words below?
Write your answers in the spaces.

mice   rice

cake   lake

nose   rose

tube   rube

Note to parent: This activity helps children to learn about long vowel sounds.

Taking away (b)

 Cross out four items on each shelf. Write how many are left.

$6 - 4 =$ **2**

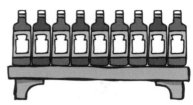

$9 - 4 =$ ☐

10 $- 4 =$ **6**

12 $- 4 =$ **8**

 Cross out five in each set. Write how many are left.

7 $- 5 =$ **2**

9 $- 5 =$ **4**

12 $- 5 =$ **7**

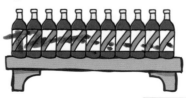

11 $- 5 =$ **6**

Note for parent: This activity gives your child practice in subtraction by taking amounts away.

Coco the clown has 12 balloons. Write the new totals in the boxes.

Sam buys 3 balloons.

12 – 3 = **10**

Coco loses 1 balloon.

9 – 1 = **8**

Lucy buys 5 balloons.

8 – 5 = **3**

Coco gives 2 balloons away.

3 – 2 = **1**

All around you

 Look at the picture.
Words are missing from some of the signs
and labels. Use the words in the box opposite
to fill in the spaces.

Café ✓ Shoe shop ✓ Open ✓ Litter ✓
Main Street ✓ Fish shop ✓ Sale ✓ Bus stop ✓
Post box ✓ Telephone ✓

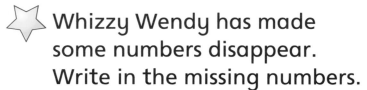

Whizzy Wendy has made some numbers disappear. Write in the missing numbers.

$3 + \bigstar = 7$

$\bigstar - 5 = 2$

$4 + \bigstar = 8$

$12 - \bigstar = 6$

$7 + \bigstar = 9$

$\bigstar - 6 = 0$

$6 + \bigstar = 8$

$11 - \bigstar = 8$

Write in the missing signs **+** or **−**.

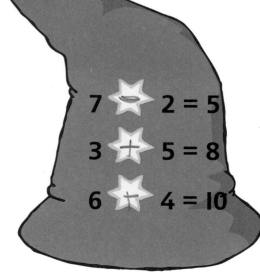

$7 \ \bigstar \ 2 = 5$

$3 + 5 = 8$

$6 + 4 = 10$

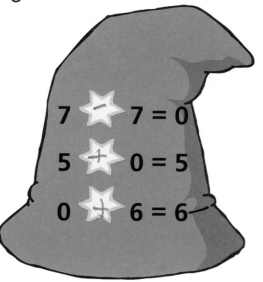

$7 \ \bigstar \ 7 = 0$

$5 + 0 = 5$

$0 + 6 = 6$

Note for parent: Encourage children to avoid using their fingers to work out these answers.

Join each broomstick to a magic star.
Colour red the star that has no broomstick.
Colour blue the star that has two broomsticks.

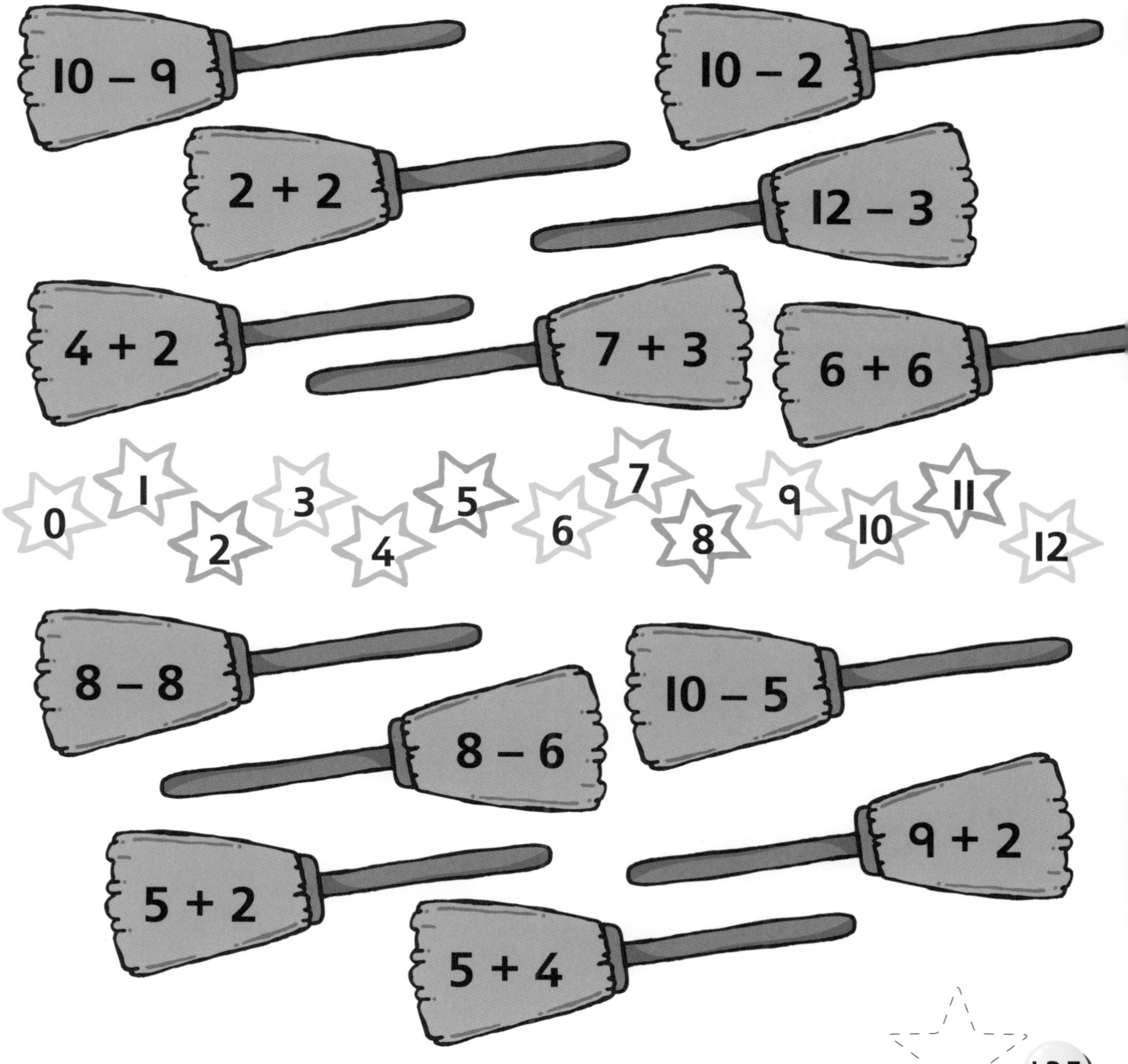

10 – 9

10 – 2

2 + 2

12 – 3

4 + 2

7 + 3

6 + 6

0 1 2 3 4 5 6 7 8 9 10 11 12

8 – 8

10 – 5

8 – 6

5 + 2

9 + 2

5 + 4

Finding words

 Draw a ring around the words you can make from the letters in the word **elephant**.

elephant

hat	put	tea	ant
pot	was	help	let
one	leap	net	had

 Now make as many words as you can from the word **aeroplane**.

I made ☐ words.

Note to parent: This activity helps children to spell simple words.

Word grid

Find the names of five animals. Find the names of five insects. The pictures will help you. Remember to look across and down.

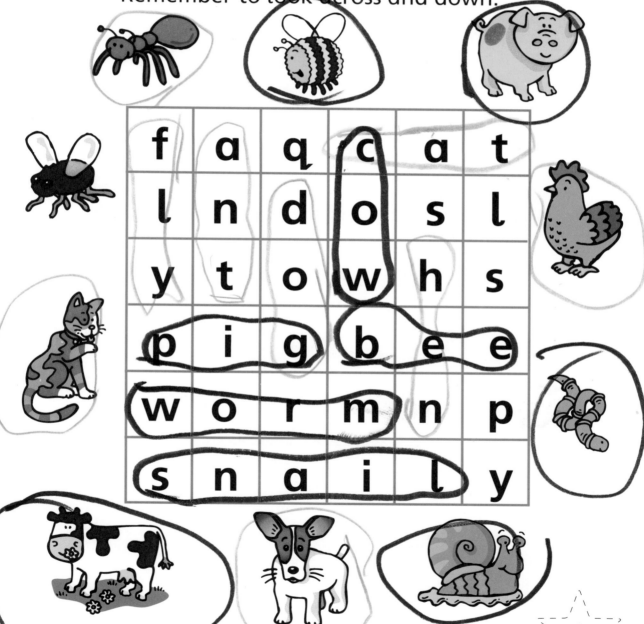

f	a	q	c	a	t
l	n	d	o	s	l
y	t	o	w	h	s
p	i	g	b	e	e
w	o	r	m	n	p
s	n	a	i	l	y

Note for parent: This activity helps children with spelling.

Counting on (b)

Use the number line to count on. Show the jumps and write the answers. The first one has been done for you.

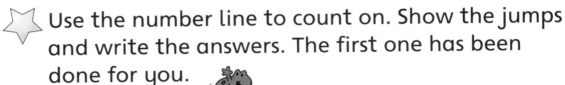

12 + 3 = **15**

10 11 12 13 14 15 16 17 18 19

8 + 4 = **12**

6 7 8 9 10 11 12 13 14 15

7 + 7 = **14**

7 8 9 10 11 12 13 14 15 16

9 + 6 = **15**

8 9 10 11 12 13 14 15 16 17

11 + 5 = **16**

9 10 11 12 13 14 15 16 17 18

Note for parent: A number line or track is useful for counting on to help add numbers.

Counting back (b)

⭐ Show the jumps and write the answers.

14 – 5 = 9

6 7 8 9 10 11 12 13 14 15 16 17

18 – 6 = 12

9 10 11 12 13 14 15 16 17 18 19 20

16 – 7 = 9

7 8 9 10 11 12 13 14 15 16 17 18

⭐ Use the number track to count back and answer these.

1 2 3 4 5 6 7 8 9 10 11 12 13 14 15 16 17 18 19 20

10 – 4 = 6   13 – 5 = 8   11 – 3 = 8

14 – 6 = 8   12 – 4 = 8   15 – 6 = 9

17 – 4 = 13   16 – 3 = 13

Note for parent: Use the number track to help
take one number from another by counting back.

139

In the dictionary

A **dictionary** tells you how to spell words. The words on this page have incorrect spellings. Look them up in a dictionary and write them correctly.

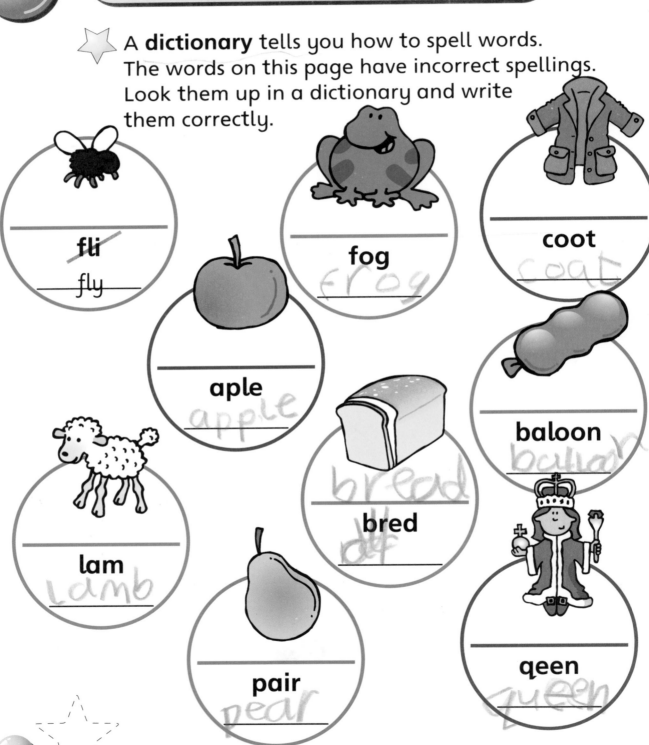

fli ~~fli~~
fly

fog
frog

coot
coat

aple
apple

bred
bread

baloon
balloon

lam
lamb

pair
pear

qeen
queen

Note to parent: This activity gives practice in learning to use a dictionary.

Dictionary skills

A dictionary also tells you what words mean. This is called a **definition**. Draw a line to join each word to the correct definition.

	boy	A creature you read about in fairy tales.
	hutch	A black-and-white bird that cannot fly.
	monster	A tool that has sharp metal teeth.
	saw	A male child.
	penguin	A pet rabbit's home.

Now draw a picture for each word to make your own picture dictionary.

Note to parent: This activity gives practice in using definitions.

Counting (c)

⭐ Join each number to its word.

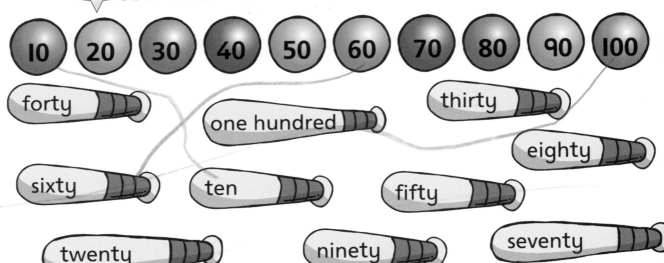

10 20 30 40 50 60 70 80 90 100

forty
one hundred
thirty
eighty
sixty
ten
fifty
twenty
ninety
seventy

Write which number comes after each of these.
Colour each even number.

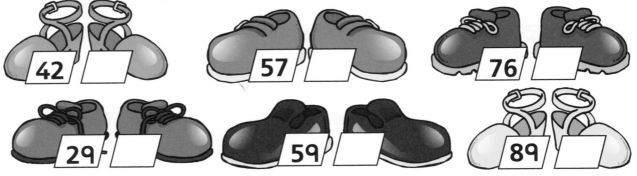

42 ☐   57 ☐   76 ☐

29 ☐   59 ☐   89 ☐

Write which number comes before each of these.
Colour each odd number.

☐ 46   ☐ 64   ☐ 85

☐ 30   ☐ 50   ☐ 70

Note for parent: This activity develops ideas of numbers up to 100, including odd and even numbers.

Missing numbers

⭐ Write in the missing numbers.

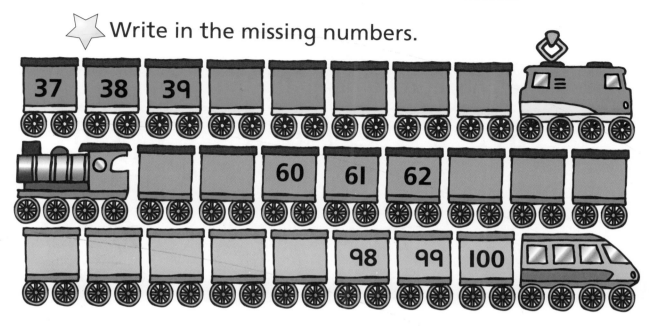

Write in the missing numbers. Colour odd
numbers red, and even numbers yellow.

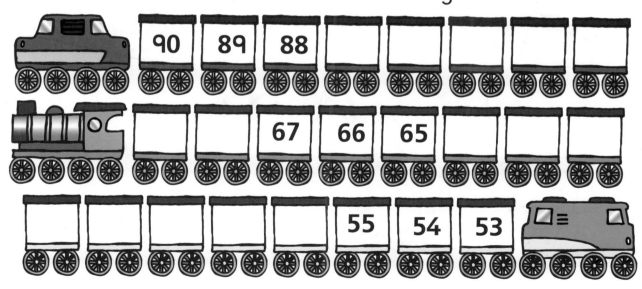

Note for parent: This activity gives further
practice with numbers up to 100.

143

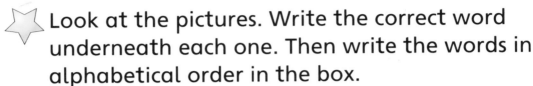

Alphabetical order 4

⭐ Look at the pictures. Write the correct word underneath each one. Then write the words in alphabetical order in the box.

a b c d e f g h i j k l m
n o p q r s t u v w x y z

web   bat   cat   fox

bed   egg

sun   owl

1	bed
2	cat
3	egg
4	fox
5	hat
6	owl
7	sun
8	web

Note for parent: This activity helps children become more familiar with alphabetical order.

Choose a middle

⭐ Choose **oo** or **ee** to finish the words below.

h oo k

c oo k

t ee th

b oo k

ch ee se

tr ee

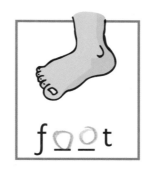
f oo t

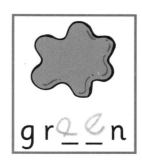
gr ee n

⭐ Fill in the spaces to complete these riddles.

teeth

You see this in the sky at night.   _ o o _

You have two of these to walk on.   _ e e _

Note for parent: Children have to listen carefully to complete this activity.

145

Machines

⭐ Total the numbers going into the machines.

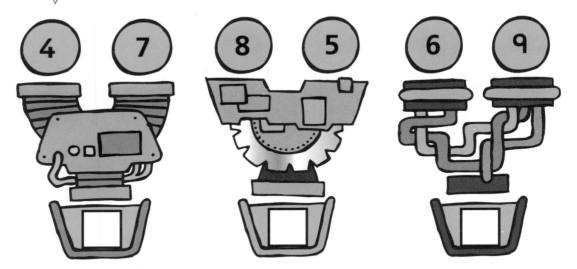

⭐ Write the numbers coming out of this machine.

7

4

8

5

9

+ 9

Note for parent: Ask your child to look at the numbers going into each machine and work out the numbers coming out.

Write the numbers coming out of these machines.

12

9

15

13

10

− 7

11

14

12

18

16

− 9

Using verbs

 A **verb** tells you what someone or something is doing. Tick the verb in each box.

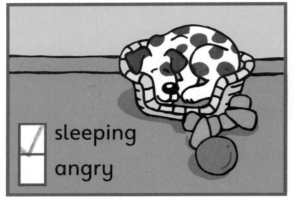

sleeping ✓
angry

happy
licking ✓

running ✓
cold

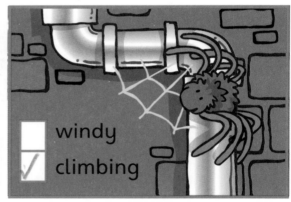

windy
climbing ✓

dirty
swimming ✓

flying ✓
fresh

What are you doing now? _____

148

Twos and tens

  Write the missing numbers in the twos pattern.

2 | 4 | 6 | 8 | 10 | 12 | 14 | 16 | 18 | 20

Write the hidden number next to each wheel.

3 × 2 = 6   5 × 2 = 10   8 × 2 = 16

2 × 10 = 20   2 × 2 = 4   2 × 7 = 14

1 × 2 = 2   9 × 2 = 18   6 × 2 = 12

Write the missing numbers in the tens pattern.

10 | 20 | 30

Write the hidden number next to each wheel.

3 × 10 = 30   6 × 10 = 60   2 × 10 = 20

10 × 4 = 40   10 × 9 = 90   10 × 10 = 100

8 × 10 = 80   1 × 10 = 10

Note for parent: This is an early start to learning multiplication tables.

Shapes

 Write the missing numbers.

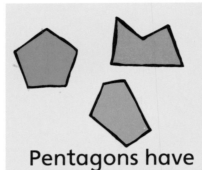

Pentagons have 5 sides.

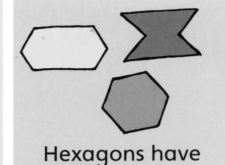

Hexagons have 6 sides.

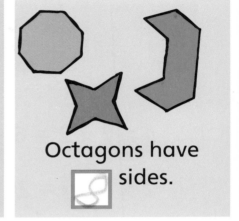

Octagons have 8 sides.

Join each shape to its name.

 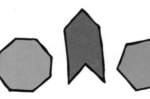 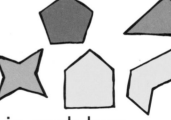

Put a cross on the odd one out in each box.

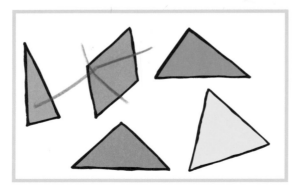 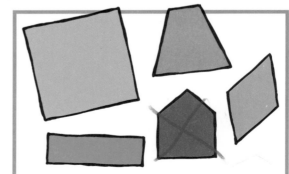

Note for parent: It is useful to know the names of 2-D and 3-D shapes.

These shapes are joined to the correct names.

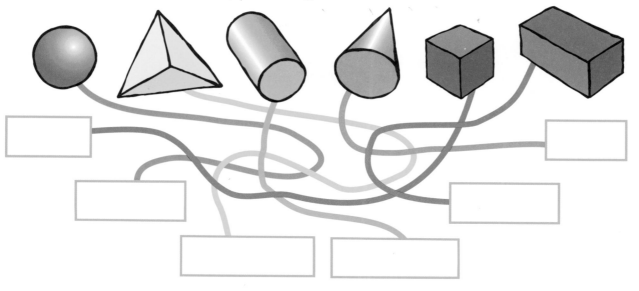

Join the shapes to their names.

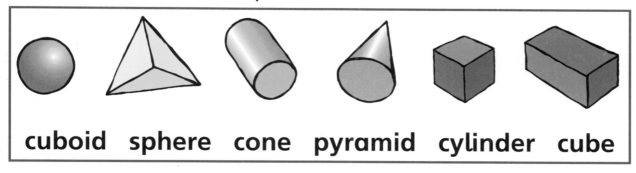

cuboid   **sphere**   **cone**   **pyramid**   **cylinder**   **cube**

Put a cross on the odd one out in each box.

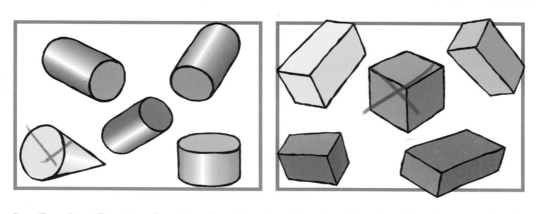

More middle sounds

⭐ Choose **ai** or **oa** to finish the words below.

n _ai_ l

b _oa_ t

c _oa_ t

g _oa_ t

s _ai_ l

t _ai_ l

sn _ai_ l

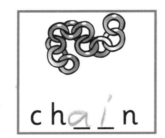

ch _ai_ n

s _oa_ p

⭐ Fill in the spaces to complete these riddles.

You get wet in this.   r a i n

You might eat this for breakfast.   _ o a _ _

152

Note to parent: This activity encourages children to listen carefully.

Rhyming picture

Look at the picture. Then write the answers to the questions.

1. What rhymes with **tall**? _ _ _ _

2. What rhymes with **bees**? _ _ _ _ _ _

3. What rhymes with **log**? _ _ _ _

4. What rhymes with **string**? _ _ _ _ _ _

5. What rhymes with **skate**? _ _ _ _

6. What rhymes with **bite**? _ _ _ _

Note for parent: This activity gives practice with double sounds at the beginning of words, and with double and treble sounds at the end of words.

153

Differences

 The difference between 4 and 9 is 5. Write the differences between the numbers below.

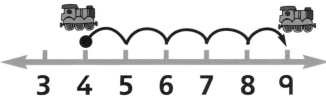

3 4 5 6 7 8 9

2 3 4 5 6 7 8 9

Difference = ☐

3 4 5 6 7 8 9 10 11

Difference = ☐

5 6 7 8 9 10 11 12

Difference = ☐

4 5 6 7 8 9 10 11 12

Difference = ☐

 What is the difference between these pairs of numbers?

9 4

Difference = ☐

6 11

Difference = ☐

⭐ Find the pairs of numbers with a difference of 6. Colour each matching pair.

12 11 6 7

13 5 9 15

⭐ Fill in the missing number so that each boat has a difference of 5. The first one has been done for you.

7 2

4

10

Months of the year

 Class 2 have made a chart to show when
the children have their birthdays.

January	February	March	April
Solomon	Brian	Alison	Imran
Duncan	Jamilla		

May	June	July	August
Ellen	Mark	Dale	Pat
Paul	Lisa	Kerry	Polly
Zara	Ahmed		Frank
Ben			

September	October	November	December
	Meena	Amy	Brendan
	Wendy		Connor
			Sally
			Gail

1. When is Amy's birthday? _____
2. When is Solomon's birthday? _____
3. When is Meena's birthday? _____
4. When is Dale's birthday? _____
5. Which month has no birthday? _____
6. Which months have the most birthdays?

_____

When is your birthday? _____

Use these letters to fill in the gaps: **ai** (nail) or **ea** (meat). Read the words when you have made them.

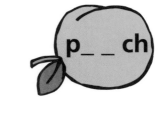

p_ _ ch

l_ _ f

sn _ _ l

s _ _ t

s_ _ l

p_ _ l

Now use these letters to fill the gaps: **oa** (goat) or **ou** (house).

b _ _ t

m _ _ se

c _ _ t

cl _ _ d

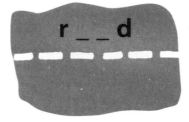

r _ _ d

Note to parent: These sounds are not easy. Read the words in brackets to help your child.

 Join each mother hen to a chick.

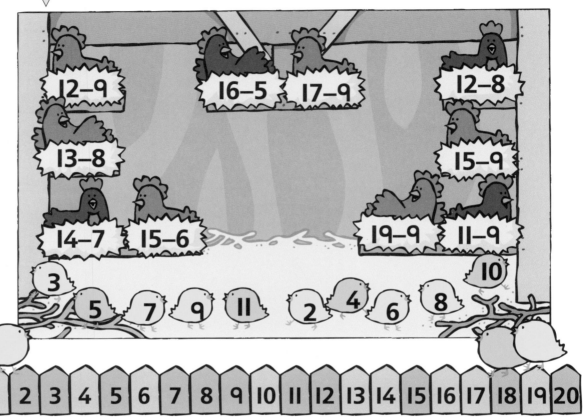

12–9   16–5   17–9   12–8

13–8   15–9

14–7   15–6   19–9   11–9

3   5   7   9   11   2   4   6   8   10

0 1 2 3 4 5 6 7 8 9 10 11 12 13 14 15 16 17 18 19 20

One egg in each basket has a different answer.
Colour the eggs that are the odd ones out.

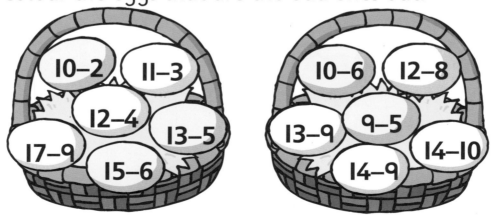

10–2   11–3
12–4
13–5
17–9
15–6

10–6   12–8
13–9   9–5
14–9   14–10

Note for parent: If children cannot work out the answers in
their head, encourage them to use the number line.

Write the missing numbers. The answers in each row must match the number on the bucket.

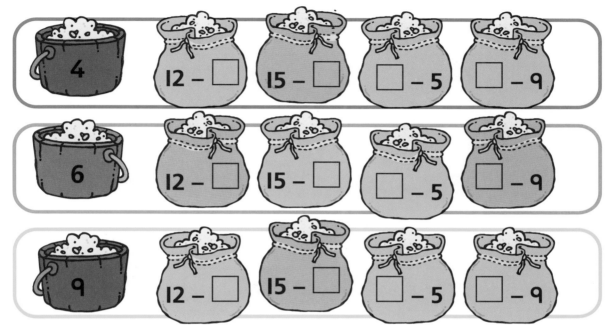

| 4 | 12 – ☐ | 15 – ☐ | ☐ – 5 | ☐ – 9 |

| 6 | 12 – ☐ | 15 – ☐ | ☐ – 5 | ☐ – 9 |

| 9 | 12 – ☐ | 15 – ☐ | ☐ – 5 | ☐ – 9 |

Subtract the smaller number from the larger one to find the difference. Write the answers in the boxes.

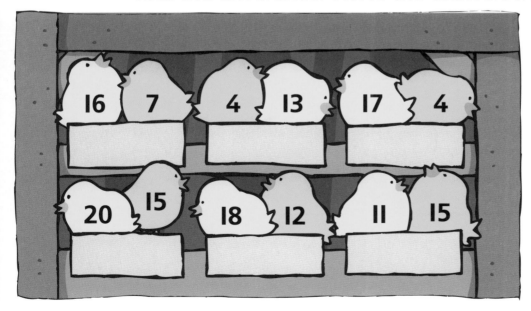

16   7   ☐   4   13   ☐   17   4   ☐

20   15   ☐   18   12   ☐   11   15   ☐

Endings

Read the word in each row. Draw a circle around two pictures that end in the same way.

bricks	comb	ducks	chicks
king	skipping rope	ring	boots
watch	hand	witch	switch
whistle	castle	bottle	belt
dress	glass	armchair	grass

Note to parent: This activity encourages children to listen carefully to the ends of words.

Making pairs

Draw a line to join two pictures that begin in the same way. Write the beginning sound under each picture.

 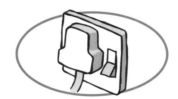 

  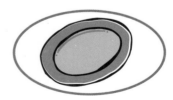

Adding to 20 (b)

 Answer each of these sums. Use the code to find the names of the four mystery vegetables.

12+4= | 16 | p

9+9= [ ] _

6+5= [ ] _

7+5= [ ] _

2+9= [ ] _

10+7= [ ] _

8+9= [ ] _

9+6= [ ] _

10+9= [ ] _

11	a
12	c
13	i
14	n
15	o
16	p
17	r
18	e
19	t
20	b

12+8= [ ] _

11+7= [ ] _

8+3= [ ] _

7+7= [ ] _

8+8= [ ] _

11+4= [ ] _

12+7= [ ] _

6+5= [ ] _

5+14= [ ] _

8+7= [ ] _

⭐ Fill in the missing numbers to complete these addition walls. The first one has been done for you.

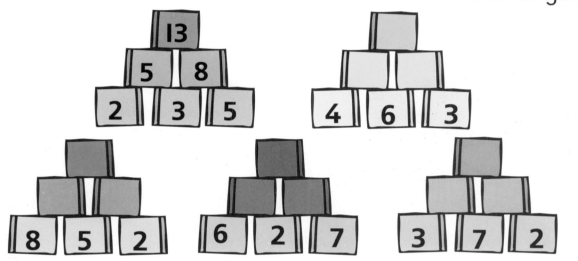

⭐ Write the numbers to complete these adding chains. The first answer has been done for you.

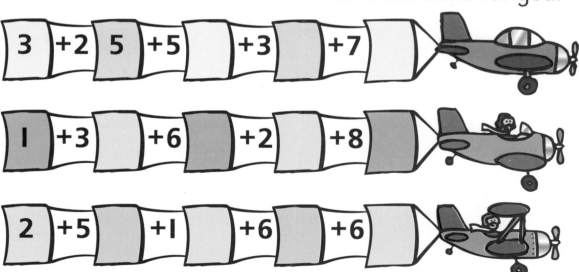

Descriptions

Look at the picture. Write a sentence saying what everyone is doing. Try to include a noun, a verb and an adjective in your sentences.

Note to parent: This activity helps children learn how to describe people using proper sentences.

Compound words

You make a compound word by joining two smaller words together.

 **+**  **=**

horse   **shoe**   **horseshoe**

Now try to make compound words from the words below:

1 star + fish = _____

2 water + fall = _____

3 home + work = _____

4 play + time = _____

5 tooth + brush = _____

6 foot + ball = _____

7 ear + ring = _____

8 book + mark = _____

Mystery numbers

 Write each answer in words. Discover the mystery number in the shaded squares.

| 0 | 1 | 2 | 3 | 4 | 5 | 6 | 7 | 8 | 9 | 10 | 11 | 12 | 13 | 14 | 15 | 16 | 17 | 18 | 19 | 20 |

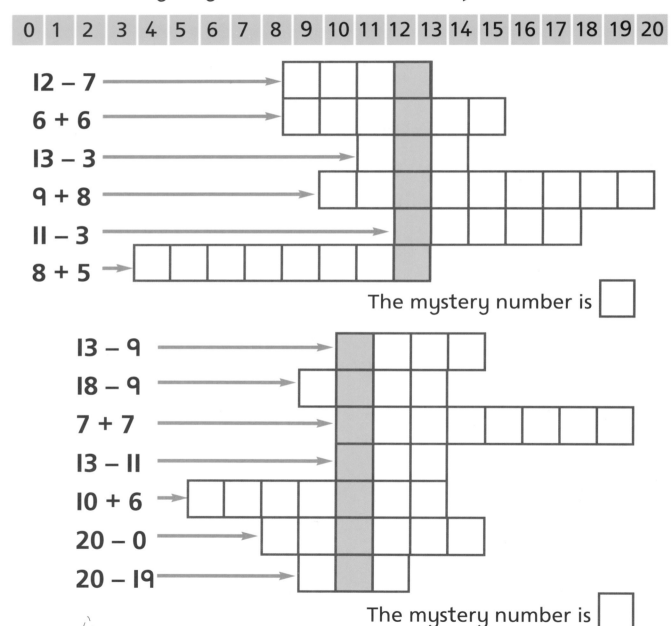

12 – 7

6 + 6

13 – 3

9 + 8

11 – 3

8 + 5

The mystery number is ☐

13 – 9

18 – 9

7 + 7

13 – 11

10 + 6

20 – 0

20 – 19

The mystery number is ☐

Note for parent: This activity gives more practice with addition and with number words.

Odd one out 2

 Work out the answers.
There is an answer in the top fish tank that is not in the bottom one. Colour this fish red.
There is an answer in the bottom fish tank that is not in the top one. Colour this fish yellow.

13 − 12
15 − 12
4 + 5
7 + 0
14 − 12
7 + 3
4 + 2
18 − 15

9 − 5
6 + 4
17 − 16
12 − 9
3 + 3
3 + 6
17 − 15

Note for parent: Children can use the number line on the facing page to help them work out the answers.

Short vowels

Write in the missing letter **a**, **e**, **i**, **o** or **u**.
These letters are called vowels.

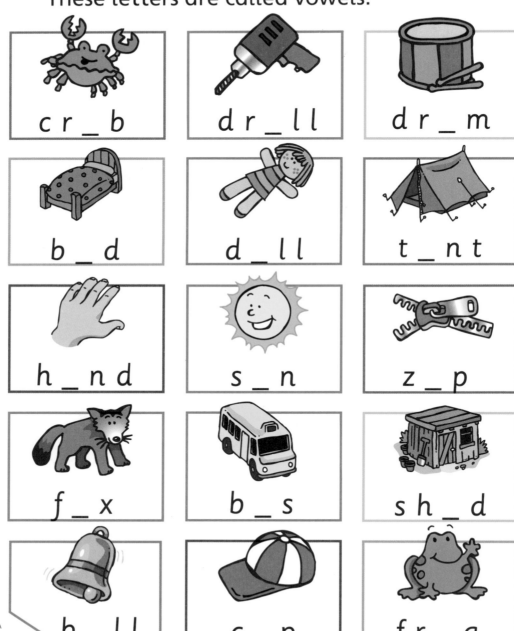

c r _ b

d r _ l l

d r _ m

b _ d

d _ l l

t _ n t

h _ n d

s _ n

z _ p

f _ x

b _ s

s h _ d

b _ l l

c _ p

f r _ g

Note for parent: This activity gives practice with short vowels.

Right or wrong?

⭐ Cross out the wrong middle sound beside each picture. Complete each word using the correct middle sound.

t _ _ t h	**ee**
	ea

n _ _ s e	**ir**
	ur

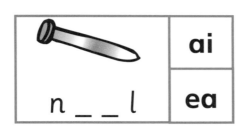

n _ _ l	**ai**
	ea

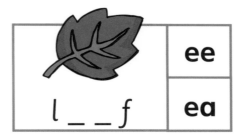

l _ _ f	**ee**
	ea

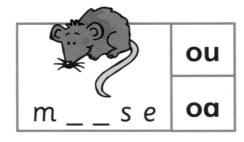

m _ _ s e	**ou**
	oa

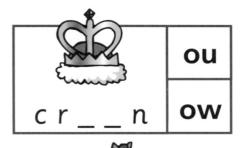

c r _ _ n	**ou**
	ow

h _ _ p	**oo**
	oa

h _ _ s e	**ur**
	or

Subtraction bonds 2

⭐ Find the different ways of making 5.

$12 - \boxed{}$

$\boxed{} - 8$

5

$9 - \boxed{}$

$\boxed{} - 6$

⭐ Find the different ways of making 6.

$\boxed{} - 4$

$9 - \boxed{}$

6

$11 - \boxed{}$

$14 - \boxed{}$

⭐ Join the shells to the correct crabs.

$15 - 8$ $17 - 9$ $14 - 6$ $13 - 9$ $11 - 4$ $12 - 8$

4   **7**   **8**

Note for parent: Show your child that answers to subtractions can be made in different ways.

 Circle the odd one out in each set.

13 − 6

18 − 9

15 − 8

14 − 7

11 − 3

15 − 7

14 − 8

13 − 5

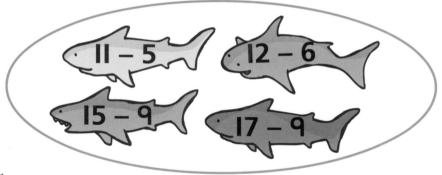

11 − 5

12 − 6

15 − 9

17 − 9

Join the matching answers.

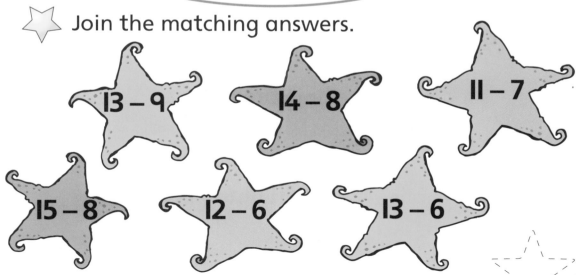

13 − 9

14 − 8

11 − 7

15 − 8

12 − 6

13 − 6

Making new words 2

You can make new words by changing some of the letters in a word.

change the **p** in **park** to **m** → **mark**
change the **p** in **park** to **sh** → **shark**

Now try to make these new words.

1. Change the **b** in **bear** to **p** → _____

                  to **w** → _____

2. Change the **f** in **fire** to **w** → _____

                  to **h** → _____

3. Change the **j** in **jaw** to **cl** → _____

                  to **str** → _____

4. Change the **br** in **brown** to **cl** → _____

                  to **cr** → _____

5. Change the **fl** in **flight** to **br** → _____

                  to **kn** → _____

Three children have made a list of what they have in their lunch box. Read the lists and then answer the questions.

Kelly
chicken sandwich
packet of crisps
apple
chocolate cake
can of fizzy drink

Sam
bottle of water
piece of cheese
yoghurt
banana
salad roll

Anna
yoghurt
carton of fruit juice
packet of raisins
cheese sandwich
chocolate biscuit

1. Who has a piece of fruit? _____

2. Who has a yoghurt? _____

3. Who has a sandwich? _____

4. Who has something made of chocolate?

   _____

5. Who likes cheese? _____

6. Who has a packet of something?

   _____

Make a separate list of what you would like to have in your lunch box.

Note for parent: This activity gives practice with comprehension and list making.

173

Patterns

 Complete the missing half of each picture.

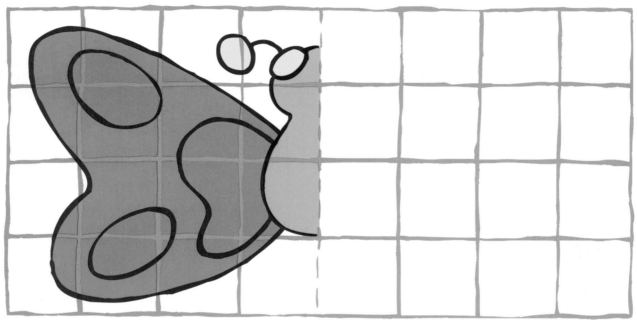

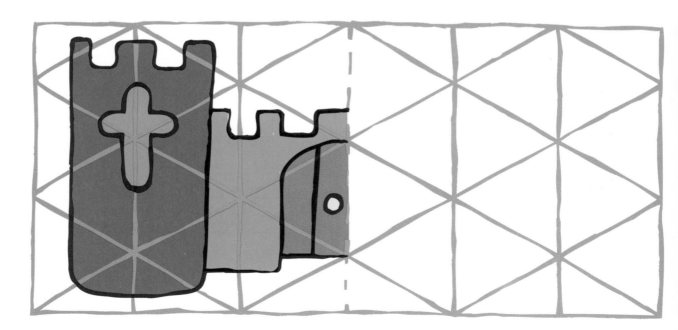

Note for parent: Ideas of pattern and symmetry are important in understanding about shape.

Colour each knight's shield to make a pattern.
Each pattern must be different.

Continue each pattern.

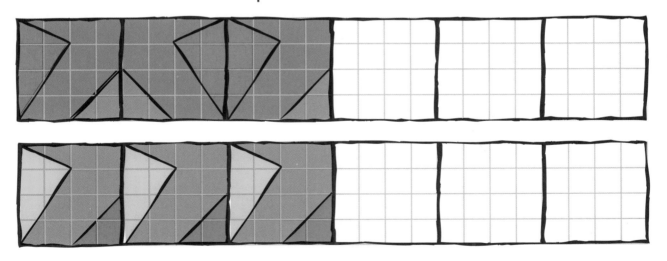

Making plurals

 Complete the plural words below. Remember that plural means 'more than one'. If a word ends in **ss,** add **es** to make the plural.

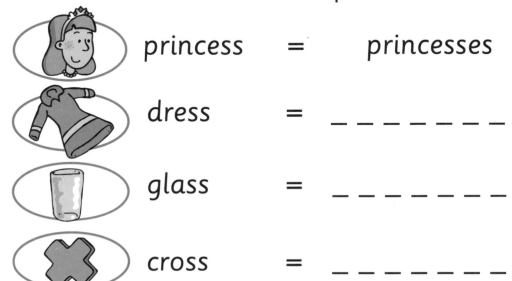

princess = princesses

dress = _ _ _ _ _ _ _

glass = _ _ _ _ _ _ _

cross = _ _ _ _ _ _ _

If a word ends in **y,** take away the **y** and add **ies.**

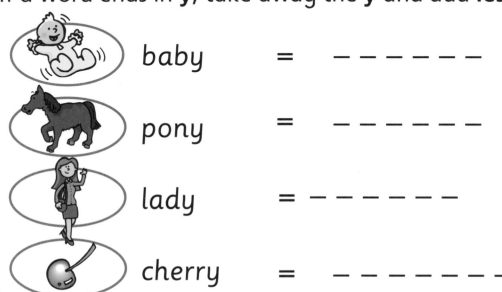

baby = _ _ _ _ _ _

pony = _ _ _ _ _ _

lady = _ _ _ _ _ _

cherry = _ _ _ _ _ _ _

Building words 1

Make four short words from each long one. Write the new words inside the balloons and then read them.

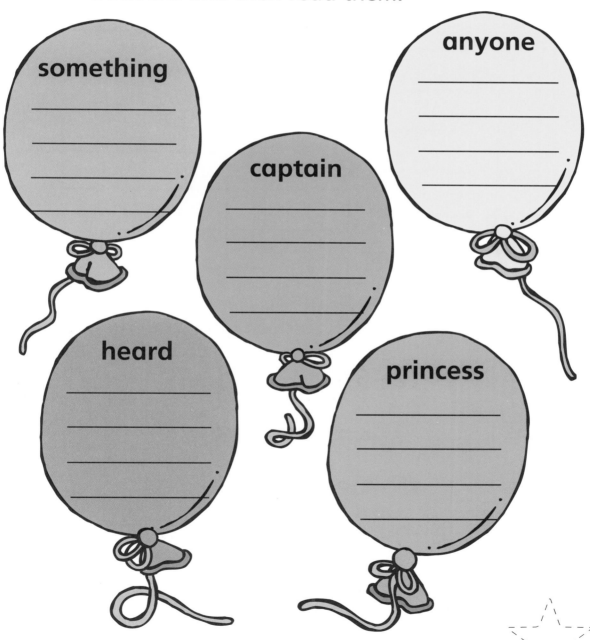

something

anyone

captain

heard

princess

Take away facts

 Write the answers to these in words. Find the mystery number in the shaded squares.

14–7 ⟶

11–6 ⟶

13–7 ⟶

17–5 ⟶

13–5 ⟶

16–15 ⟶

16–7 ⟶

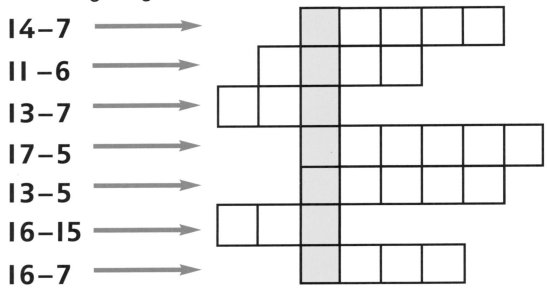

 Answer these as quickly as you can. Time yourself and try to beat your best time.

9 – 4 = ☐   12 – 6 = ☐   8 – 4 = ☐

8 – 7 = ☐   7 – 4 = ☐   13 – 8 = ☐

11 – 6 = ☐   15 – 10 = ☐   6 – 2 = ☐

7 – 5 = ☐   9 – 6 = ☐   10 – 5 = ☐

10 – 7 = ☐   11 – 4 = ☐   14 – 7 = ☐

Note for parent: These activities give practice in learning the subtraction facts within 20.

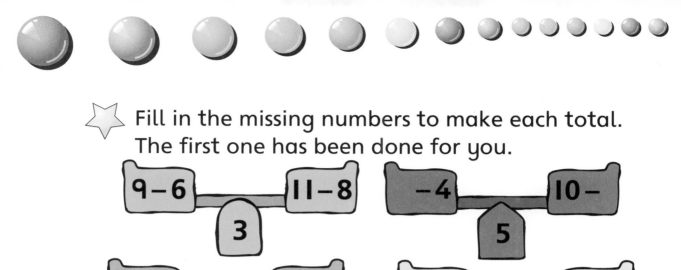

⭐ Fill in the missing numbers to make each total. The first one has been done for you.

9 – 6 ⸺ 11 – 8
3

– 4 ⸺ 10 –
5

– 2 ⸺ 14 –
6

11 – ⸺ – 9
4

⭐ Write in your own numbers to make the total.

___ – ⸺ ___ –
7

⭐ Complete the number trails back to zero.

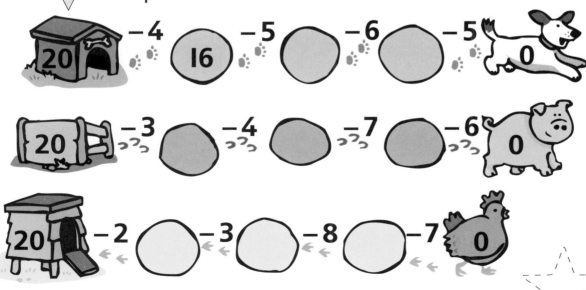

20 –4 16 –5 ◯ –6 ◯ –5 0

20 –3 ◯ –4 ◯ –7 ◯ –6 0

20 –2 ◯ –3 ◯ –8 ◯ –7 0

Speech marks

⭐ Read what each animal says.

I like to fly and sing.

I have a long trunk.

I like to jump and hop.

I have a long tail.

I like to eat hay.

Write what each animal said using speech marks.
Here is an example: Dog said, "I like to run."

1. Parrot said, "_____."

2. Monkey said, _____.

3. Horse said, _____.

4. Kangaroo said, _____.

5. Elephant said, _____.

Missing letters

 Sometimes when we talk to people we do not say every word.

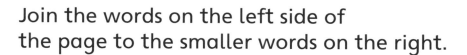

I am = I'm

It is = It's

Join the words on the left side of the page to the smaller words on the right.

is not	I'd
cannot	won't
I would	isn't
I am	I'm
will not	you've
you have	can't

Write these sentences again using smaller words instead of the underlined words:

<u>I would</u> like to see you but <u>I am</u> ill. I <u>cannot</u> go out but <u>I would</u> like to see you if you have time and <u>it is</u> not too far for you to come.

_____

_____

_____

_____

Tens and ones

⭐ Write the missing numbers using tens and ones.

15 = 10 + ☐   31 = 30 + ☐   64 = 60 + ☐

16 = 10 + ☐   39 = 30 + ☐   73 = 70 + ☐

19 = 10 + ☐   42 = 40 + ☐   85 = 80 + ☐

12 = ☐ + 2   36 = ☐ + 6   71 = ☐ + 1

25 = ☐ + 5   47 = ☐ + 7   89 = ☐ + 9

28 = ☐ + 8   57 = ☐ + 7   92 = ☐ + 2

13 = ☐ + ☐   43 = ☐ + ☐   62 = ☐ + ☐

26 = ☐ + ☐   48 = ☐ + ☐   75 = ☐ + ☐

Tick the smaller number in each pair.

Note for parent: This shows how large numbers are built up using tens and ones.

Words and numbers

 Write the correct number on each child.

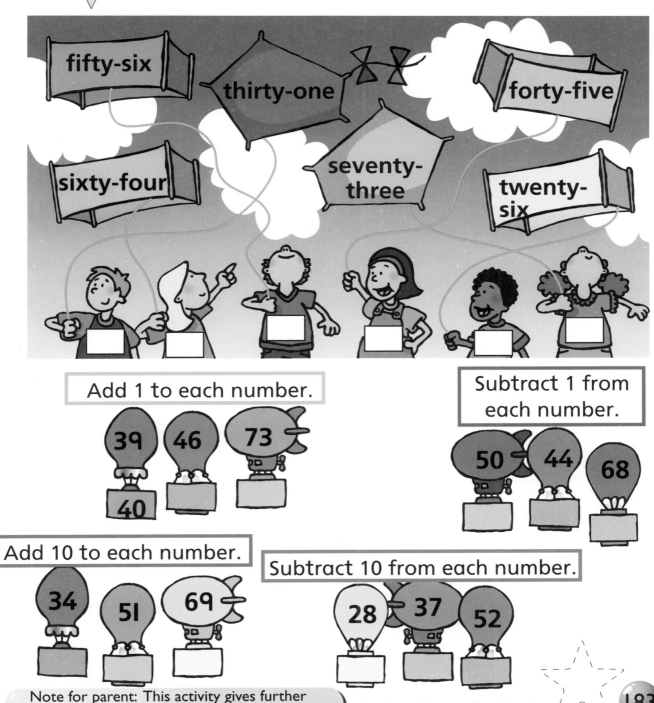

Add 1 to each number.

39 → 40
46
73

Subtract 1 from each number.

50
44
68

Add 10 to each number.

34
51
69

Subtract 10 from each number.

28
37
52

Note for parent: This activity gives further practice in working with large numbers.

Sound alike

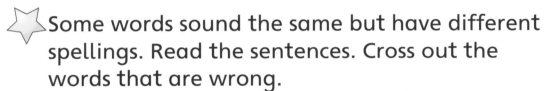

⭐ Some words sound the same but have different spellings. Read the sentences. Cross out the words that are wrong.

I could not **see/sea** the moon.

I have **too/two** feet.

You can watch the stars at **knight/night.**

I had a **knew/new** bike for my birthday.

You can **right/write** a letter with my pen.

⭐ Can you write a sentence using each of these words?

way _____

_____

weigh _____

_____

Note to parent: This activity helps children to understand that some words sound the same but have different spellings.

Say the name of each picture. Draw a line to join two pictures to make one word. Write the new words. You can use a dictionary to help you.

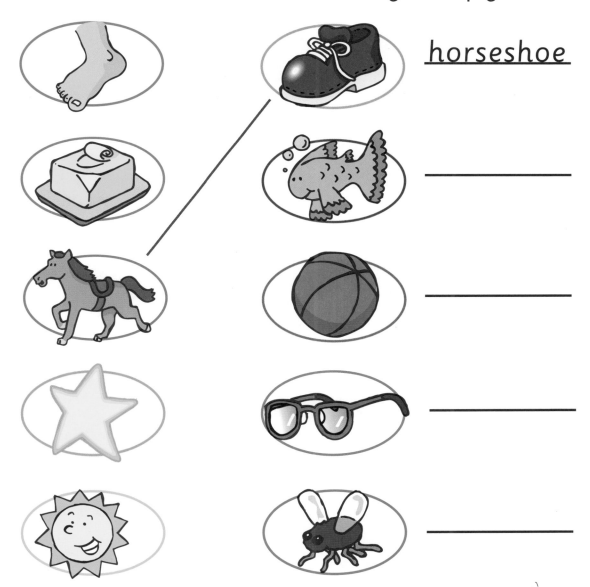

horseshoe

_____

_____

_____

_____

Note for parent: This activity helps children to make one word from two separate words.

185

Add three numbers

★ Find the total of the three numbers.
Write the total in the centre.

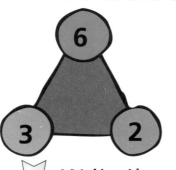 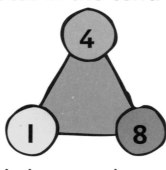 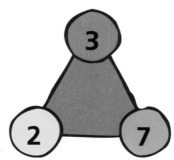

★ Write the missing numbers.

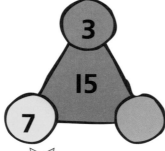 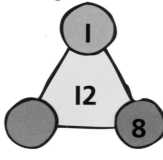 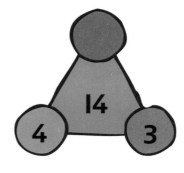

★ Write a number in each shape. Make each triangle equal 20. The first one has been done for you.

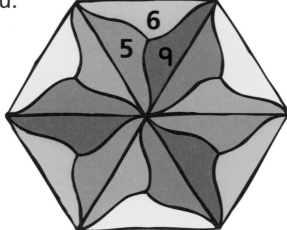

Note for parent: When adding three numbers, look for pairs of numbers that are easy to add and then add on the third number.

Money totals

 How much money is in each purse? Write the answers in the boxes.

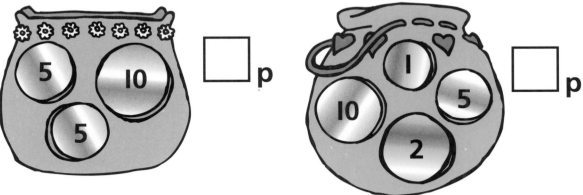

□ p   □ p

 What is the total cost of each group of items? Write the answers in the boxes.

£3 £4 £6 £7 £5

£ □

£ □

£ □

Note for parent: This activity gives practice in totalling coins and exact pounds.

Writing postcards

 Write a postcard to a relative (for example your granny, a cousin, an uncle) telling them about your school.

Dear _____

Draw a picture that might be on the other side of the postcard, or cut out a picture and stick it here.

Note for parent: Postcard writing is good practice.

Speech bubbles

⭐ Look at what is happening in each picture.
What do you think the people are saying?
Write the words in the speech bubbles.

Treble sounds

⭐ Read the beginning sounds. Draw a circle around two pictures that start in the same way.

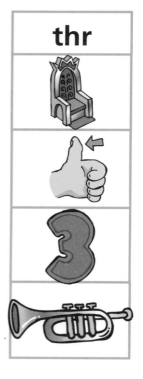

thr

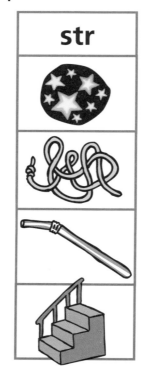

str

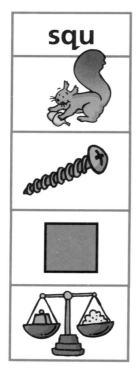

squ

 Read the sentences. Think of the missing word and write it. Use a dictionary to help you.

I thr _ _ the ball in the air.

A small river is called a str _ _ _.

A mouse squ _ _ _ _.

Note to parent: This activity helps children to identify the treble beginning sounds thr, str and squ.

Opposites 1

⭐ What are the opposites of the words below?
Each answer is the opposite of the clue word.
Fill in the word grid. You can use a dictionary
to help you.

ACROSS		DOWN	
1. little	4. light	1. dry	4. happy
2. cold	5. fat	2. front	5. full
3. open	6. clean	3. new	6. low

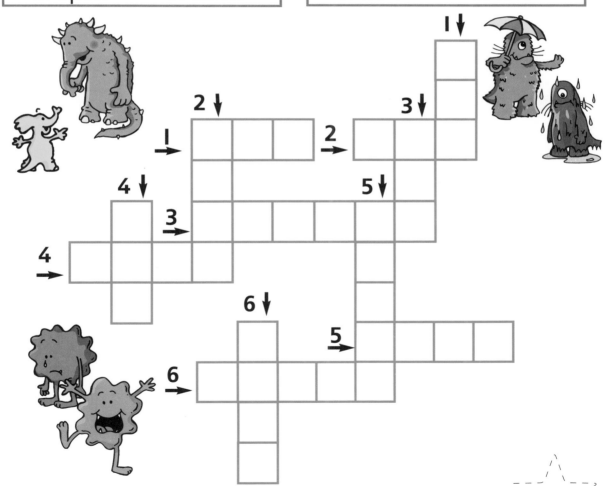

Note for parent: This activity helps children to learn about
opposites. It also gives practice in using a dictionary.

Doubles

⭐ Answer these doubles as quickly as you can.

4 + 4 = ☐

6 + 6 = ☐

3 + 3 = ☐

5 + 5 = ☐

8 + 8 = ☐

2 + 2 = ☐

7 + 7 = ☐

10 + 10 = ☐

9 + 9 = ☐

⭐ Use the doubles above to help answer these.
Join the sums to the correct answers.

3 + 4

10 + 9

5 + 6

5 + 4

6 + 7

8 + 9

8 + 7

7
9
11
13
15
17
19

Note for parent: If your child is quick with doubles, he or she can use
this to work out 'near doubles' e.g. 6 + 6 is 12, so 6 + 7 is one more.

Giving change

Draw coins to show the change from 20p.
Write the amount of change.

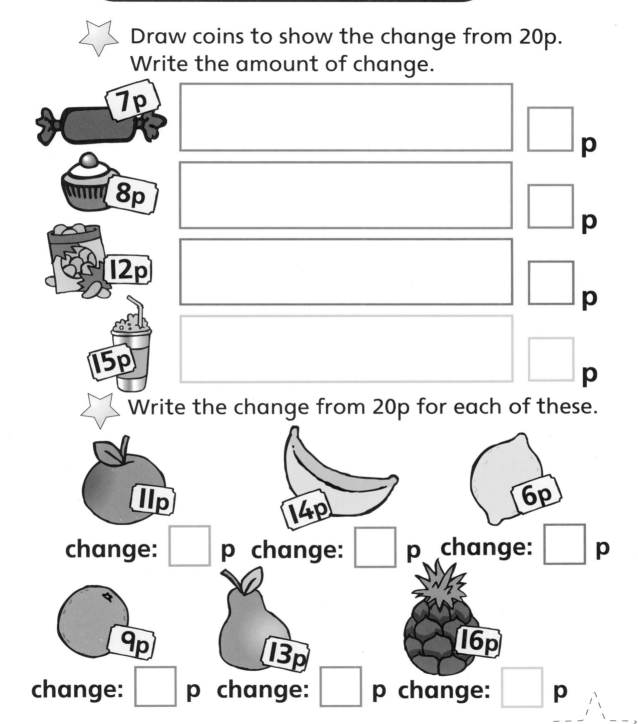

7p [ ] p

8p [ ] p

12p [ ] p

15p [ ] p

Write the change from 20p for each of these.

11p change: [ ] p

14p change: [ ] p

6p change: [ ] p

9p change: [ ] p

13p change: [ ] p

16p change: [ ] p

Note for parent: To work out the amount of change your child needs to count on from the price up to 20p.

193

Reading instructions

☆ Read the instructions and then draw on the pictures.

1. Draw a hat on the first clown.
2. Draw long shoes on the second clown.
3. Draw spots on the trousers of the third clown.
4. Draw a flower on the hat of the second clown.
5. Draw curly hair on the third clown.
6. Draw a smile on the face of the first clown.
7. Draw a bow-tie on the first clown and the third clown.
8. Draw buttons on the shirts of the second clown and the third clown.

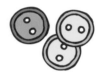

Note for parent: This activity gives practice in following instructions.

Silly or sensible? 2

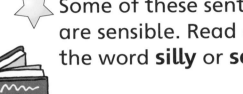

Some of these sentences are silly, and some are sensible. Read each one and then write the word **silly** or **sensible** beside it.

1. A library is a place to borrow babies. _____

2. Clocks help us to tell the time. _____

3. All boys have black hair. _____

4. Teachers like to teach bananas. _____

5. Cats have baby puppies. _____

6. There are lots of animals at the zoo. _____

Now write two sentences yourself:

A silly sentence: _____

_____

A sensible sentence: _____

_____

Note for parent: In this activity children can practise responding to different sentences.

195

 Write the missing numbers on the clock face.

Make the clock
show 7 o'clock.

Make each of these clocks and watches
show 4 o'clock.

Make each of these clocks and watches
show half-past two.

Note for parent: Telling the time on all kinds of clocks and watches is important.

One hour passes on each clock. Write the new times.

Join clocks that say the same time.

Draw in the missing minute hand
on each clock.

5:45   9:15   6:30   4:15

Building words 2

Fill in the missing letters. The pictures will help you.

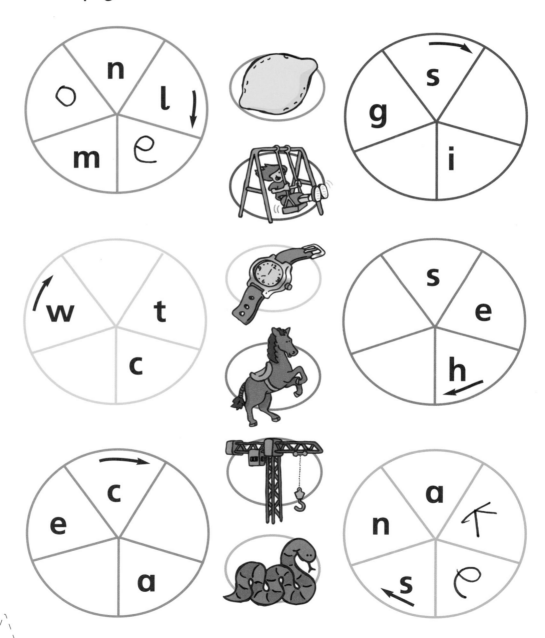

Two together

 Join two parts to make a word. Write the whole word and then draw a picture of it.

ch   arf   _____

sn   air   _____

sc   ail   _____

dr   umpet   _____

fl   um   _____

tr   ower   _____

Large numbers

Write the missing numbers in these patterns.

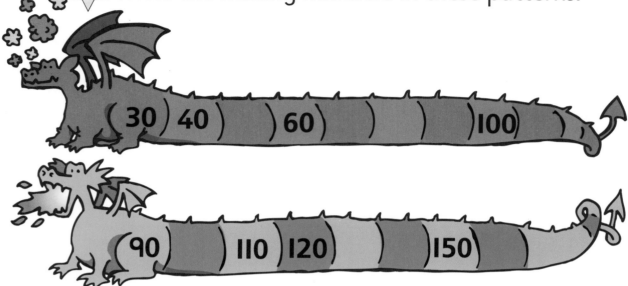

(30) 40)) 60))) 100))

(90)) 110)120)))150))

Write the totals in the boxes. Use the first answer to help you work out the second answer.

7+2= ☐

70+20= ☐

4+3= ☐

40+30= ☐

3+5= ☐

30+50= ☐

6+5= ☐

60+50= ☐

Note for parent: This activity gives practice in adding multiples of 10. Look at the pattern between the addition facts and the multiples of 10.

Draw a line to match each dragon to the correct cave.

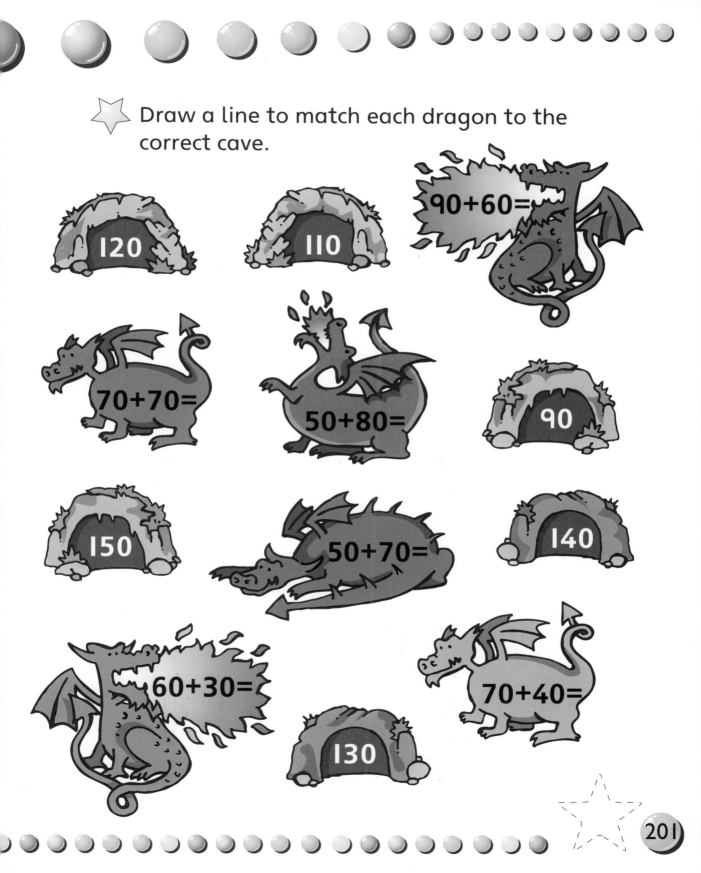

120

110

90+60=

70+70=

50+80=

90

150

50+70=

140

60+30=

130

70+40=

Opposites 2

An **antonym** is a word that has the opposite meaning to another word.

big   **small**   **happy**   **sad**

Read the words in the box.

pull√	near√	dry√	cold√	full√
hard√	long√	light√	last√	day√

Use the words in the box to write the antonym of each word in this list.

1 wet *dry*
2 soft *hard*
3 first *last*
4 far *near*
5 empty *full*

6 hot *cold*
7 night *day*
8 push *pull*
9 short *long*
10 heavy *light*

Finish the sentences

 Draw a line to join the beginning of each sentence to the correct ending.

1. The dog barked   into the air.

2. The horse galloped   a big web.

3. The frog jumped   on the wall.

4. The birds flew   at the burglar.

5. The spider spun   across the field.

6. The cat slept   out of the pond.

Now finish these sentences.

The dolphin jumped _____ .

The kangaroo hopped _____ .

Fives, twos and tens

⭐ Write the missing numbers on the fives pattern.

5 10 15 20 25 30 35 40 45 50

Write the hidden number beside each leaf.

 1 x 5 = 5

 3 x 5 = 15

9 x 5 = 45

5 x 5 = 25

5 x 6 = 30

5 x 2 = 10

8 x 5 = 40

4 x 5 = 20

x 5 = 35

Write how many fives are in each group.

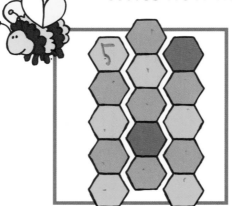

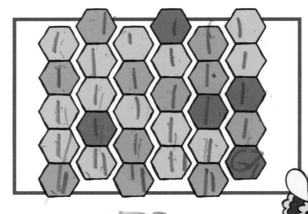

 75 fives

 150 fives

Note for parent: Your child can start learning the 2x, 5x and 10x tables.

Write in the answers to these tables.

2	x 1	=	2	2	x 10	=	20	5 x 9 =	45
2	x 2	=	4	5	x 1	=	5	5 x 10 =	50
2	x 3	=	6	5	x 2	=	10	10 x 1 =	10
2	x 4	=	8	5	x 3	=	15	10 x 2 =	20
2	x 5	=	10	5	x 4	=	20	10 x 3 =	30
2	x 6	=	12	5	x 5	=	25	10 x 4 =	40
2	x 7	=	14	5	x 6	=	30	10 x 5 =	50
2	x 8	=	16	5	x 7	=	35	10 x 6 =	60
2	x 9	=	18	5	x 8	=	40	10 x 7 =	70

Work out the answers. Join each saucer to a cup.

Riddles 2

Write the answer that rhymes. Draw a picture in each box. Make up your own rhyme for the last box using **ou** in the middle.

You eat ice cream with this. It rhymes with **moon.**	_ _ _ _ _
This is a green vegetable. It rhymes with **tea.**	_ _ _
This animal moves very slowly. It rhymes with **tail.**	_ _ _ _ _
You wear this outdoors. It rhymes with **boat.**	_ _ _ _

Note to parent: This activity involves simple reading and recognition of rhyme.

Dictionary practice

This is a page from a picture dictionary. Complete the missing parts. The first one has been done for you.

kennel	A kennel is a small house for a dog.
kettle	You can boil water in a kettle.
key	_____ _____
kite	A kite flies in the air. It is joined to a long piece of string.
kitten	_____ _____
knife	A knife is a sharp tool. You use a knife to cut your food.

Note for parent: This activity helps children to understand and use dictionary skills.

Addition bonds (b)

 Make these totals in different ways. The first one has been done for you.

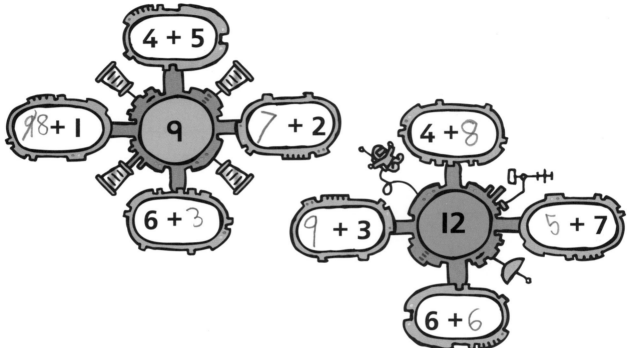

4 + 5

98 + 1

9

7 + 2

6 + 3

4 + 8

9 + 3

12

5 + 7

6 + 6

 Write your own numbers for this spaceship.

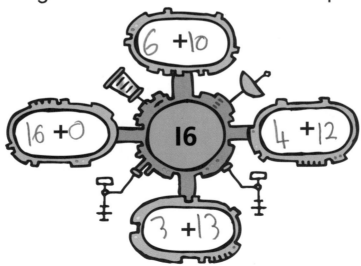

6 + 10

16 + 0

16

4 + 12

3 + 13

Note for parent: Addition bonds are all the different ways that a total can be made with two numbers.

Hidden numbers (b)

 Leaves have hidden some of the numbers on the snakes. Write the missing numbers.

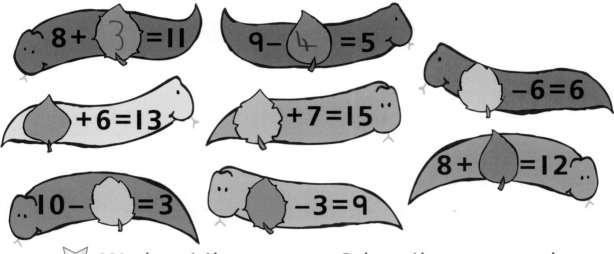

8 + 3 = 11

9 − 4 = 5

− 6 = 6

+ 6 = 13

+ 7 = 15

8 + = 12

10 − = 3

− 3 = 9

⭐ Work out the answers. Colour the even numbers red. Colour the odd numbers blue. Which number is hidden in the picture?

7−6	3+4	4+3		9−4	
	7−5	2+1	8−2	7+7 / 11−5	14−9
11+6			8−7		
		6+6	10+3		3+4
1+8	4+6	5+6	9−3	10−6	11+7
		6+3	8+7		7+6
13−6	9−7			9−4	4+4
				3+6	8−3
12−5	8+4	9+4	9+9	11−7	12−3
6−1		4+9		3+2	

Note for parent: This activity gives practice in adding and taking away numbers to 20.

Word search

Look for these words in the grid below.

nouns	**verbs**	**adjectives**
dog ✓	run	cold
tree	grows ✓	tall
mouse	squeaks	soft

a	e	m	c	i	g	r	t	h	j
s	r	l	c	b	t	a	l	q	k
d	o	g	s	g	r	o	w	s	z
f	k	f	m	u	e	s	b	g	s
d	g	s	t	d	e	q	n	q	u
r	u	n	l	l	f	u	d	m	p
p	x	o	l	j	y	e	u	o	n
w	c	l	o	o	v	a	l	u	t
y	a	z	e	v	n	k	y	s	b
t	h	x	a	e	c	s	w	e	d

Now find all the letters of the alphabet and colour them red. There are 26 to find.

Note for parent: This activity helps children to recognize nouns, verbs and adjectives.

A puzzle page

Make as many words as you can from the letters.

p	o	r
(l	e	t)
i	s	a
r	e	m

You can move in any direction but do not jump a square.

_____   _____

_____   _____

_____   _____

_____   _____

_____

How many words did you find?

Change one letter to make a new word.

man   _____   You cook food in this.

coat   _____   You go on water in this.

robber   _____   You rub out with this.

card   _____   A horse can pull this.

fork   _____   Soldiers live in this.

wolf   _____   This is a sport.

211

Sharing

⭐ Join the balls to the clowns.
Each clown must have the same
number of balls.

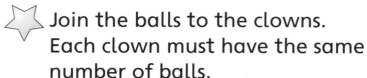

3 balls for
each clown

3 balls for
each clown

2
balls for
each clown

Write how many twos are on each branch.

2 twos

3 twos

Write how many threes are on each pond.

☐ threes

☐ threes

Write how many fours are in each bag.

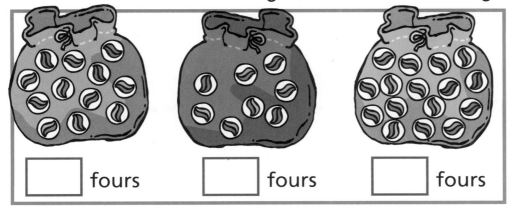

☐ fours   ☐ fours   ☐ fours

Rhyming words

Find a word in the balloon that rhymes with each word in the basket. Write the rhyming word in the basket.

made

tea

hare

head

meat

train

fly

wood

would _wood_   bed _head_

meet _meat_   maid _made_

hair _hare_   sigh _fly_

me _tea_   plane _train_

Note for parent: This activity introduces rhyming words with a different spelling pattern.

⭐ Look carefully at the pictures on the book covers. Make up a title for each book and write it on the cover. Colour the pictures.

Space race.

night light.

wich go.

chirken hunt.

Note for parent: This activity encourages children to read and understand book titles.

More subtraction

 Complete these number trails.

120 –10 ☆ –20 ☆ –10 ☆ –30 ☆

150 –20 ☆ –30 ☆ –10 ☆ –10 ☆

180 –10 ☆ –20 ☆ –30 ☆ –40 ☆

 Answer these sums. Use the first answer to help you work out the second answer.

8 – 3 = 5
80–30= 50

7 – 4 = 3
70–40= 30

15 – 8 = 7
150+80= 170

9 – 5 = 4
90–50= 40

12 – 7 = 5
120–70= 150

14 – 6 = 8
140–60= 180

Note for parent: This activity gives practice in subtracting multiples of 10.

Colour the flying saucers with the same answer.
Use a different colour for each matching pair.

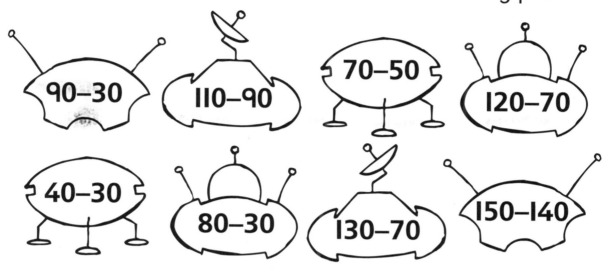

90–30

110–90

70–50

120–70

40–30

80–30

130–70

150–140

Draw a line to join the numbers with a difference of 50.

110

40

130

80

170

90

60

120

Odd one out 3

 Cross out the word that does not belong in each row.

1	Monday	May	Friday	Tuesday	Sunday
2	square	triangle	circle	shape	rectangle
3	paint	red	orange	blue	~~green~~
4	~~sheep~~	~~horse~~	~~pig~~	~~cow~~	~~lion~~
5	bus	car	man	lorry	van

Now put the words in the correct group.

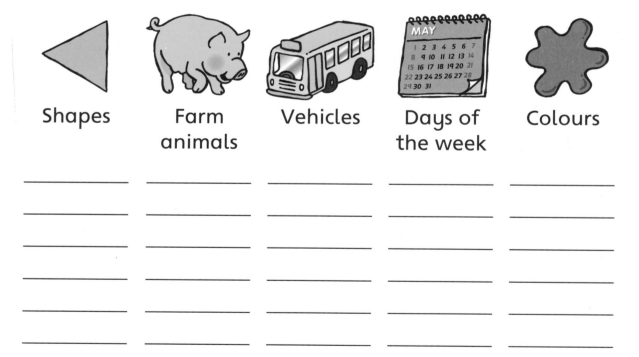

Shapes   Farm animals   Vehicles   Days of the week   Colours

_____   _____   _____   _____   _____

_____   _____   _____   _____   _____

_____   _____   _____   _____   _____

_____   _____   _____   _____   _____

_____   _____   _____   _____   _____

_____   _____   _____   _____   _____

Can you add two words of your own to each list?

Second chance

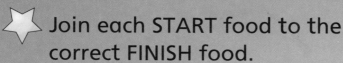

Join each START food to the correct FINISH food.

START

 add on 0 =5

 add on 3 =6

 add on 6 = 8

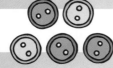 add on 6 =10

Join each START group to the correct FINISH group.

START

take away 3 =2

take away 2 =2

take away 0 =6

take away 5 =1

 =29

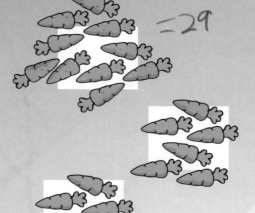

FINISH

 =11

Note for parent: This activity helps children to remember about adding and taking away.

Second chance

★ Join the sounds to the pictures.

cl

dr

sn

bl

gr

sp

st

sw

Gold Stars worker!

Note for parent: Here is a second chance to remember double sounds.

Second chance

 Fill in the missing letters and pictures. You can choose your own pictures

 Choose one of these beginning sounds to complete the words in the boxes.

dr   sp   cl

d r a g o n

c l o w n

Super star!

s p o o n

Note for parent: This page gives a chance to see what children can remember from earlier pages.

221

Second chance

 Write the missing number in each star.

$6 + 3 = 9$ $3 + 3 = 6$ $6 - 6 = 0$ $9 - 3 = 6$

$5 + 5 = 10$ $4 + 4 = 8$ $5 - 4 = 1$ $12 - 4 = 8$

$8 + 3 = 11$ $6 + 5 = 11$ $8 - 0 = 8$ $10 - 5 = 5$

$4 + 8 = 12$ $3 + 9 = 12$ $11 - 8 = 3$ $9 - 9 = 0$

Colour all the odd numbers.

13   18   24   33   49   65   76   81   85   94

Finish writing the names of the shapes.

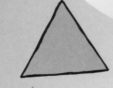

t riangel   p exigon.   h exigon.

c one   c ubid   p irimied

Note for parent: This page gives children a chance to see
what they can remember from the first half of the book.

Second chance

 See what you can remember.

Make these words shorter.

is not   I would   cannot

_____   _____   _____

Sort these words into the three boxes below.

~~dog~~   ~~tall~~   ~~grows~~   ~~soft~~   ~~mouse~~
~~run~~   ~~tree~~   ~~cold~~   ~~squeaks~~

nouns

dog
tree
mouse

verbs

Squeaks
grows
run.

adjectives

soft
cold
tall

Well done!

Note for parent: This page gives children a second chance to remember.

Second chance

⭐ Write the first two letters.

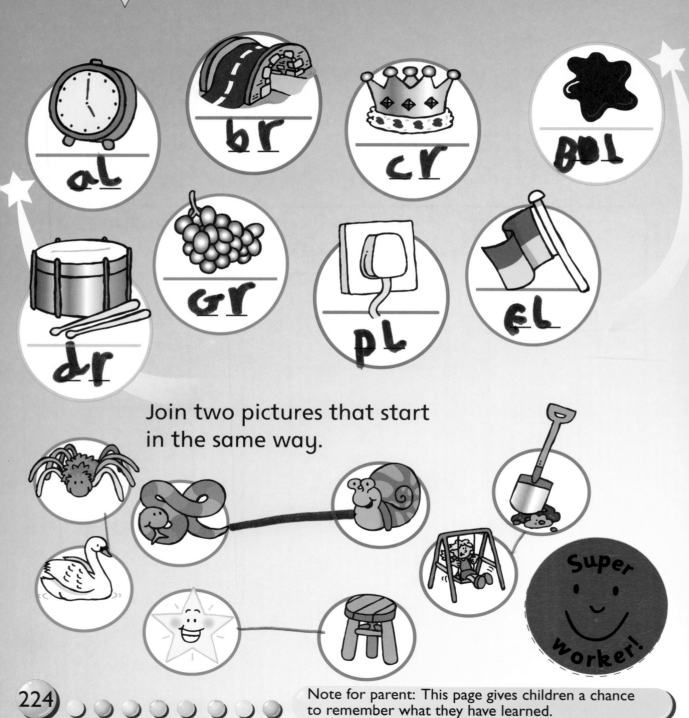

al

br

cr

Bbl

dr

Gr

pL

EL

Join two pictures that start
in the same way.

Super
worker!

Note for parent: This page gives children a chance
to remember what they have learned.

Second chance

Read each riddle and write the answer. You can ask an adult to help you.

The words in the box will help you find the right answer.

sheep **shell** **ship**

1. This sails across the sea. _ship_

2. You find this on a farm. _sheep_

3. You find this on the beach. _shell_

Add the letter **s** when there is more than one. Write the whole words in the spaces.

cow

cows

farmer

farmers

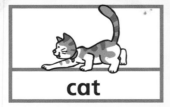
cat

cats

I'm a star!

Note for parent: This page tests what children remember from earlier pages.

225

Second chance

 See what you can remember.

Read the words.
Write the number.

two	2
six	6
three	3
eight	8
ten	10
four	4
seven	7
nine	9
one	1
five	5

Join each word ending to a picture.

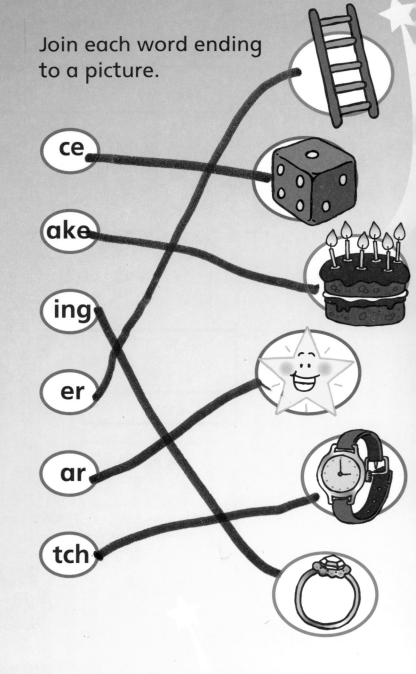

ce

ake

ing

er

ar

tch

⭐ Join the sums to the correct totals.

5+2   4+1   4+4

5   8   7

⭐ Draw how many balls come out of the machines.

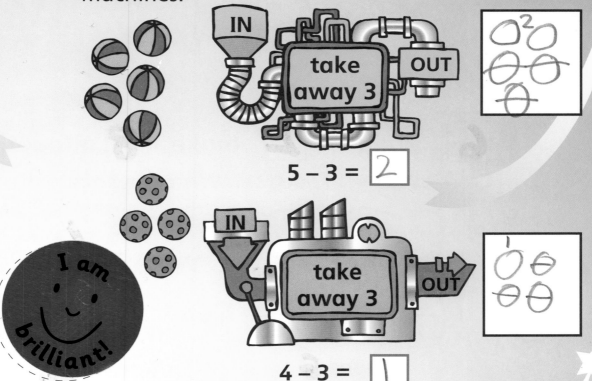

IN   take away 3   OUT

$5 - 3 = \boxed{2}$

IN   take away 3   OUT

$4 - 3 = \boxed{1}$

I am brilliant!

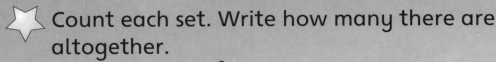

Second chance

⭐ Count each set. Write how many there are altogether.

  **9** sweets altogether

  **6** cakes altogether

⭐ Count the spots on each monster. How many are there altogether?

6 and **2** make **8** altogether

⭐ Cross out two in each set. Write how many are left.

Well done!

8 take away **2** leaves **6**

4 take away **2** leaves **2**

Second chance

⭐ Look at the first picture in each row.
Draw a ring around another picture that has the same ending.

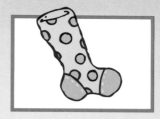

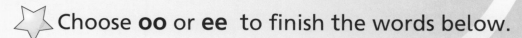

⭐ Choose **oo** or **ee** to finish the words below.

h**oo**k

c**oo**k

t**ee**t h

Note to parent: This activity is a chance to see what children have remembered.

229

Second chance

⭐ Subtract the smaller number from the larger one to find the difference. Write the answers in the boxes.

20+6
26

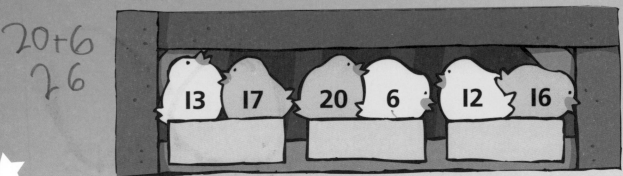

13 17   20 6   12 16

Colour all the sacks that have EVEN answers.

12 + 8   12 − 6   11 + 6   15 + 3   20 + 15   18 + 12   15 + 11

Write the missing numbers.

twenty-six = 20 + 6   forty-eight = 40 + 8
seventy-nine = 70 + 9   thirty-two = 30 + 2
sixty-five = 60 + 5   eighty-four = 80 + 4

Join the matching answers. Ring the odd one out.

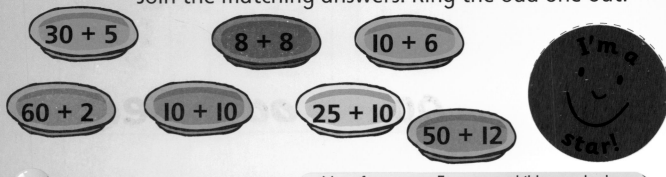

30 + 5   8 + 8   10 + 6

60 + 2   10 + 10   25 + 10   50 + 12

I'm a Star!

Note for parent: Encourage children to look back if they cannot remember what to do.

⭐ Count each set. Write the total.

 5 **+** **5** **=** **10**

⭐ Cross out four items on each shelf. Write how many are left.

6 − 4 = **2**   **10** **− 4 =** **6**

⭐ Write the numbers coming out of this machine.

11 **2**
14 **5**
12 **3**
− 9
18 **9**
16 **7**

I am brilliant!

Note for parent: This page is a chance to find out what your child can remember.

231

Second chance

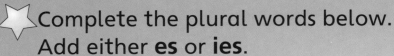

⭐ Complete the plural words below.
Add either **es** or **ies**.

glass = _ _ _ _ _ _ _

dress = _ _ _ _ _ _ _

baby = _ _ _ _ _ _

pony = _ _ _ _ _ _

⭐ Fill in the missing letters. The pictures will
help you.

Note to parent: This activity is another chance to
see what children have remembered.

Answers

Page 16-17

The missing letters are:

c f g i l

n r u x y .

Page 18-19

Page 20

dog, fox, log;

hat, bat, fan;

bell, web, dress;

sum, sun, bus;

six, pig, lips.

Page 21

m<u>a</u>n, r<u>e</u>d, p<u>i</u>g, s<u>o</u>ck, j<u>e</u>t, d<u>u</u>ck, b<u>u</u>s, b<u>e</u>d,

l<u>o</u>g, f<u>i</u>sh, cr<u>a</u>b, m<u>e</u>n.

Page 22

clockwise from top left: 8 spots, 10 spots, 6 spots, 4 spots, 7 spots, 9 spots.

Page 23

clockwise from top left: frog 1 needs 1 extra spot, frog 2 needs 6 extra spots, frog 3 needs no extra spots, frog 4 needs 4 extra spots, frog 5 needs 5 extra spots, frog 6 needs 2 extra spots, frog 7 needs 3 extra spots.

Page 24

The missing letters are:

b c e g h j k m.

Page 25

<u>car</u>pet, <u>tooth</u>brush, <u>sh</u>ed, teleph<u>one</u>, caterpillar, f<u>or</u>k, c<u>up</u>, sp<u>oo</u>n, <u>sh</u>eet, m<u>an</u>.

Page 26

Page 27

There is more than one possible answer. Parents need to check their child's answers for this page.

Page 28

Row 1: book; row 2: tree; row 3: cat; row 4: house; row 5: bicycle.

Page 29

The teacher is under the table. ✗

A girl is reading a book. ✓

A boy is painting the door. ✗

The teacher is looking at the children. ✓

A cat is reading a book. ✗

A boy has got a brush. ✓

The hamster is on its cage. ✗

Page 30

3 and 2 make 5 altogether, 2 and 4 make 6 altogether.

buttons: 1 + 6 = 7; stars: 4 + 3 = 7; sweets: 5 + 2 = 7; hearts: 6 + 3 = 9.

Page 31

3 + 5 = 8, 4 + 4 = 8, 1 + 5 = 6, 2 + 5 = 7.

Page 32

ball/wall, balloon/moon, bee/tree, nail/snail, carrot/parrot.

Page 33

<u>f</u>lag, <u>d</u>ragon, <u>c</u>lock, <u>f</u>lower, <u>c</u>lown, <u>s</u>poon, <u>g</u>rapes, <u>d</u>rum.

Pages 34-35

6 biscuits altogether, 6 cakes altogether, 5 pizzas altogether, 7 ice creams altogether, 9 sweets altogether. 3 and 2 make 5 altogether, 4 and 3 make

7 altogether, 6 and 2 make 8 altogether.

Page 38

row 1: 4 take away 2 leaves 2; 6 take away 2 leaves 4; 5 take away 2 leaves 3.

row 2: 8 take away 2 leaves 6; 7 take away 2 leaves 5; 10 take away 2 leaves 8.

row 3: 3 − 2 = 1, 2 − 2 = 0, 9 − 2 = 7.

Page 39

Page 40

The missing letters are:

o r s u x y.

Page 41

tr–triangle, dr–drum, ch–chair, gl–glove, cl–clock, br–brush, cr–crayons, sc–scarf, fl–flowers, bl–blanket.

Page 42

5 take away 2 leaves 3, 6 take away 2 leaves 4, 8 take away 2 leaves 6, 4 take away 2 leaves 2, 9 take away 3 leaves 6.

Page 43

5 children, 4 chairs, difference = 1.

7 children, 5 chairs, difference = 2.

6 children, 3 chairs, difference = 3.

Page 44

<u>c</u>lock, <u>b</u>ridge, <u>c</u>rown, <u>b</u>lack; <u>g</u>reen, <u>p</u>lug, <u>d</u>rill, <u>f</u>lag.

Page 45

sp: spider, spoon, spade;

st: stool, stamp, star;

sn: snail, snake, snowman;

sw: swan, sweater, swing.

Page 46

Page 48

h<u>a</u>t, s<u>u</u>n, m<u>o</u>p, n<u>e</u>t, p<u>i</u>g, c<u>u</u>p, v<u>a</u>n, f<u>o</u>x, six.

Page 49

line 1: 2 rabbits are hidden,
line 2: 1 rabbit is hidden,
line 3: 4 rabbits are hidden,
line 4: 5 rabbits are hidden.

Pages 50-51

4 sweets add 2 sweets = 6 sweets;
6 sweets add 1 sweet = 7 sweets;
5 sweets add 3 sweets = 8 sweets;
7 sweets add 2 sweets = 9 sweets.
6 drinks take away 1 drink = 5 drinks;
5 drinks take away 3 drinks = 2 drinks;
3 drinks take away 2 drinks = 1 drink;
7 drinks take away 4 drinks = 3 drinks.

Pages 52

Everyone fell over and the turnip came out. **D**
The farmer saw an enormous turnip. **A**
Everyone tried to pull up the turnip. **C**
The farmer tried to pull up the turnip. **B**

Pages 54

row 1 are cubes; row 2 are cylinders, row 3 are spheres, row 4 are cuboids.

Pages 55

Kitchen: pan / knife / frying pan / spoon / food processor.
Garden: spade / wheelbarrow / watering can / fork / lawnmower.

Page 56

bat–cat, fox–box, jar–car,
dog–log.

Page 57

butterfly/ but, fly; hand/ and; heart/ear, art; window/ win;
snail/ nail; caterpillar/ cat, ill.

Pages 58-59

$2 + 3 = 5$, $3 + 4 = 7$, $4 + 5 = 9$.
$3 + 5 = 8$ altogether, $4 + 2 = 6$ altogether. $3 + 2 = 5$, $2 + 2 = 4$,
$4 + 3 = 7$, $5 + 1 = 6$, $6 + 3 = 9$, $4 + 5 = 9$.

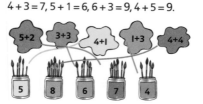

Page 60

ball, dog, cat; bcd.
house, fish, girl; fgh.
ladybird, moon, key; klm.
rabbit, queen, parachute; pqr.
umbrella, seesaw, television; stu.

Page 61

or – fork, us – bus, an – man, all – ball, am – lamb, in – twins, at – bat.

Page 62

△ triangle, ○ circle, ▭ rectangle, ☐ square.

Page 63

red bags = ✗; yellow bags = ✓.

Page 64

bridge/brick, skeleton/skier,
dragon/dress, grass/grapes,
clown/cloud.

Page 65

clock, slide, train, spider, twins, frog.

Pages 66-67

$7 – 2 = 5$, $5 – 2 = 3$, $8 – 2 = 6$. Parents need to check their child's answer for the last sum on page 18. 5 balls take away 3 balls = 2 balls, 4 balls take away 3 balls = 1 ball, 8 balls take away 4 balls = 4 balls.

Page 68

A little <u>girl</u> put on her dress.
The <u>sun</u> was hot.
I like getting into my <u>bed</u> to go to sleep.
I can see a bird's nest in the <u>tree</u>.
Dad kicked the <u>ball</u>.
A little <u>boy</u> put on his football boots.

Page 69

What is the time?
I like to eat chips.
When do I go to school?
The car was going fast.
Who went up the hill with Jill?
The cat likes to sit on my lap.
There are 8 capital letters.

Page 70

$1 + 4 = 5$, $3 + 3 = 6$, $4 + 6 = 10$.
$4 + 6 = 10$, $8 + 2 = 10$.

Page 71

$4 + 3 = 7$, $2 + 5 = 7$, $6 + 2 = 8$, $3 + 3 = 6$, $6 + 3 = 9$, $1 + 5 = 6$.
total of 4: red and yellow scarves; total of 6: orange and dark-blue scarves; total of 7: pink and bright-blue scarves; total of 10: green and purple scarves.

Page 72

fish, egg, duck – def; ice cream, horse, goat – ghi; key, lemon, jellyfish – jkl; nurse, orange, moon – mno.

Page 73

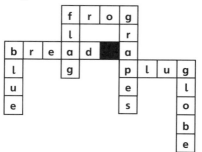

Pages 74-75

$4 + 2 = 6$, $5 + 3 = 8$, $7 + 2 = 9$,
$3 + 4 = 7$, $6 + 4 = 10$, $2 + 3 = 5$.
$5 + 2 = 7$, $4 + 1 = 5$, $3 + 3 = 6$,
$6 + 3 = 9$, $3 + 1 = 4$.
The missing numbers are:
rocket 1 – 6, 9, 10; rocket 2 – 1, 3, 4, 8;
rocket 3 – 8, 9, 12, 15.

Pages 76

Alison, Duncan, Imran, Jamilla, Meena, Patrick, Samuel, Wendy.

Pages 77

Wednesday, Saturday, Thursday, Friday, Sunday, Tuesday, Monday.

Pages 78

$4 – 2 = 2$, $7 – 3 = 4$, $8 – 5 = 3$, $5 – 2 = 3$, $7 – 4 = 3$.

Pages 79

$4 – 1 = 3$, $5 – 3 = 2$, $8 – 7 = 1$, $5 – 5 = 0$, $9 – 5 = 4$, $10 – 2 = 8$. $10 – 5$ and $5 – 0$; $8 – 7$ and $6 – 5$; $10 – 7$ and $6 – 3$.

Page 80

bus, pig, bee, cup, saw, car.

Page 81

1. ship, 2. sheep, 3. shoes,
4. shark, 5. shell, 6. shorts.

Pages 82–83

6 − 3 = 3, 5 − 2 = 3, 8 − 4 = 4,
9 − 3 = 6, 10 − 2 = 8, 7 − 6 = 1.

Pages 85

9827, 9026, 9146, 9544.
Ms Walker
Mr Anderson
Mrs Todd
Mrs Depster

Pages 86

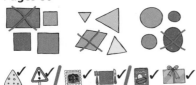

Pages 87

rectangles, triangles, circles, squares

Page 88

bus, dog, bat, drum, crab, fork, cup, ten.

Page 89

Possible answers are: cherries/chocolate,
train/tractor, straws/strawberries,
swan/switch, drum/drawing,
crocodile/crayons.

Pages 90–91

6: 0 + 6, 1 + 5, 2 + 4. 8: 1 + 7, 2 + 6, 3 + 5. 9:
1 + 8, 2 + 7, 3 + 6. 7: 0 + 7, 1 + 6, 2 + 5.

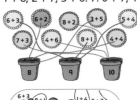

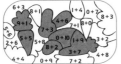

A rabbit and a carrot are hidden
among the shapes.

Pages 92

elephant
A large animal with a long trunk
and ivory tusks. It lives in Africa and
Asia.

kangaroo
A large animal that can jump very
well. It carries its young in a pouch.
It comes from Australia.

monkey
A small animal with long arms and
feet that it uses like hands. It lives in
jungles.

panda
A black and white animal like a
bear. It lives in China.

zebra
An animal like a horse with black
and white stripes. It lives in Africa.

Pages 93

giraffes, penguins, whales, bears,
turtles.
10, 4, 20, 18, 14.

Pages 94

11 o'clock, 8 o'clock, 5 o'clock.

Pages 95

From left to right: half-past 4, half-past
10, half-past 7.

Page 96

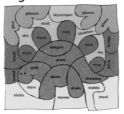

dinosaur

Page 97

ducks, pigs, cows, farmers, cats.

Pages 98–99

4 + 3 = 7, 6 + 2 = 8, 5 + 5 = 10, 9 + 1 = 10,
7 + 2 = 9, 3 + 5 = 8, 2 + 4 = 6, 4 + 4 = 8,
6 + 3 = 9. The missing numbers are:
row 1 − 6, 8. row 2 − 10, 9, 8, 10.
4 + 3 = 7, 3 + 2 = 5, 4 + 5 = 9, 6 + 3 = 9,
2 + 8 = 10, 5 + 3 = 8, 6 + 2 = 8, 3 + 3 = 6,
3 + 7 = 10. The missing totals are: train
1 − 6, 9; train 2 − 3, 6, 8; train 3 − 3, 4, 7.

Pages 102

Top train: 9, 10, 11, 12, 13, 14, 15, 16, 17.
Middle train: 11, 12, 13, 14, 15, 16, 17, 18,
19, 20. Bottom train: 7, 8, 9, 10, 11, 12, 13,
14, 15, 16.
eleven–11, fourteen–14, twelve–12,
fifteen–15, twenty–20, sixteen–16,
thirteen–13, seventeen–17.

Pages 103

clockwise from top left: rhinoceros, tiger,
monkey, elephant.

Page 104

str + ing = string, tr + ain = train, bl +
ack = black, gl + asses = glasses, ch +
erries = cherries,
scr + ew = screw.

Page 105

star/car, sock/duck, fish/brush,
dice/mice, switch/witch.

Pages 106–107

6 − 4 = 2, 7 − 3 = 4, 5 − 1 = 4, 8 − 5 = 3, 6 − 3
= 3, 9 − 4 = 5, 10 − 5 = 5, 7 − 4 = 3, 8 − 3 = 5.
The number 4 is hidden in the grid.

7 − 4 = 3, 6 − 2 = 4, 5 − 3 = 2, 8 − 4 = 4, 6 − 3
= 3, 7 − 2 = 5, 9 − 6 = 3, 9 − 5 = 4, 10 − 4 = 6.

Page 108

cub/cube, pip/pipe, fir/fire, cap/cape.

Page 109

transport: car/bus/train;
food: banana/bread/apple; animals:
tiger/giraffe/lion.

Page 110

8 + 3 = 11, 9 + 5 = 14, 8 + 7 = 15,
6 + 7 = 13, 9 + 9 = 18, 6 + 4 = 10.
10 + 3 = 13, 10 + 5 = 15, 10 + 8 = 18,
10 + 6 = 16, 10 + 10 = 20, 10 + 1 = 11.

Page 111
12 – 8 = 4, 12 – 6 = 6, 13 – 4 = 9,
11 – 9 = 2, 16 – 8 = 8, 12 – 5 = 7.
20 – 6 = 14, 20 – 4 = 16, 20 – 5 = 15,
20 – 7 = 13, 20 – 8 = 12, 20 – 2 = 18.

Page 112

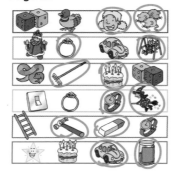

Page 113
sn: snail/snow/snake;
cr: crocodile/crayon/crab;
sp: spider/spade/spoon;
fl: fly/flower/flag.

Page 115

Page 116-117
2+2=4, 3+4=7, 6+3=9, 3+5=8,
4+5 =9, 6+6=12. 5+5 and 6+4 (=10), 3+1
and 2+2 (=4), 5+2 and 6+1 (=7), 5+4 and
6+3 (=9).
Odd one out is 6+5.
3+5=8, 2+8=10, 5+7=12, 7+4=11, 4+5=9.
+2 machine: IN: 3, 0; OUT: 9, 6. +4
machine: IN: 6, 8; OUT: 6,8,9.

Page 118
wall/bell, sock/clock, ring/swing,
hammer/ladder.

Page 119
well, lock, king, letter.

Page 120
3: 4 – 1, 7 – 4, 3 – 0, 9 – 6, 8 – 5.
4: 7 – 3, 5 – 1, 9 – 5, 8 – 4, 6 – 2.
Possible answers are: 6 – 1, 8 – 3, 9 – 4.

Page 121
7+5=12, 9+11=20, 8+3=11, 10+8=18,
6+8=14, 8+9=17. Red spaceships are:
6+8, 6+4, 6+6, 9+9, 8+8, 7+7, 10+10.

Page 122-123
4 + 5 = 9, 6 + 4 = 10, 3 + 5 = 8,
5 + 5 = 10

6 + 4 = 10

5 + 7 = 12

7 + 3 = 10

4 + 8 = 12, 3 + 9 = 12, 7 + 5 = 12,
6 + 6 = 12.

Page 124
1. The boy is reading a book.
2. The girl is looking at the television.
3. The dog is playing with a ball.
4. The man is cutting the grass.

Some of the nouns are:
1. sofa, lamp, mug, shoes.
2. slippers, book, video.
3. tree, house, grass.
4. lawnmower, flowers, boots, hat.

Page 125
1. A ladybird is very small. 2. The leaves
fell off the tree because it was windy.
3. The sun was shining and the sky was
blue. 4. Dad had just picked the flowers
so they were fresh. 5. The dog was
happy because he had a new ball.
6. It was cold in the garden and there
was ice on the pond.

Page 126
9–3=6, 6–4=2. 9-6=3, 5-3=2, 12–7=5,
12–6=6, 10–6=4. No-one catches the
fish 11–2.

Page 127
11–3=8, 10–3=7, 6–3=3, 5–3=2.
7–5=2, 12–5=7, 5–5=0, 9–5=4.

Page 128
star, scarf, barn, shark, card.

Page 129
cub/cube, cap/cape.
mice/dice, cake/lake, nose/rose,
tube/cube. There are other possible
answers.

Page 130-131
6 – 4 = 2, 9 – 4 = 5, 10 – 4 = 6, 12 – 4 = 8,
7 – 5 = 2, 9 – 5 = 4, 12 – 5 = 7, 11 – 5 = 6.
12 – 3 = 9, 9 – 1 = 8, 8 – 5 = 3, 3 – 2 = 1.

Page 132-133

Page 134-135
3+4=7, 7–5=2, 4+4=8, 12–6=6, 7+2=9,
6–6=0, 6+2=8, 11–3=8.
7–2=5, 3+5=8, 6+4=10, 7–7=0,
5+ or –0 =5, 0+6=6.
10–9=1, 10–2=8, 2+2=4, 12–3=9, 4+2=6,
7+3=10, 6+6=12.
8–8=0,10–5=5, 8–6=2, 5+2=7, 9+2=11,
5+4=9. The 3 star has no broomstick.
The 9 star has two broomsticks (12–3=9,
5+4=9).

Page 136
elephant: hat, tea, ant, help, let, leap,
net.
aeroplane: plane, plan, an, leap, rope,
ran, pan, pea, pear. You may find more
words.

Page 137

Page 138
12 + 3 = 15, 8 + 4 = 12, 7 + 7 = 14,
9 + 6 = 15, 11 + 5 = 16.

Page 139
14 – 5 = 9, 18 – 6 = 12, 16 – 7 = 9.
10 – 4 = 6, 13 – 5 = 8, 11 – 3 = 8, 14 – 6 = 8,
12 – 4 = 8, 15 – 6 = 9, 17 – 4 = 13,
16 – 3 = 13.

Page 140
fog = frog; coot = coat; aple = apple; lam
= lamb; bred = bread; baloon = balloon;
pair = pear; qeen = queen.

Page 141

boy = A male child. **hutch** = A pet rabbit's home. **monster** = A creature you read about in fairy tales. **saw** = A tool that has sharp metal teeth.
penguin = A black-and-white bird that cannot fly.

Page 142

10–ten, 20–twenty, 30–thirty, 40–forty, 50–fifty, 60–sixty, 70– seventy, 80–eighty, 90–ninety, 100–one hundred. 43, 58, 77, 30, 60, 90. Even numbers are: 42, 58, 76, 30, 60, 90. 45, 63, 84, 29, 49, 69. Odd numbers are: 45, 63, 85, 29, 49, 69.

Page 143

Above: red train 40, 41, 42, 43 ,44; green train 58, 59, 63, 64, 65; blue train 93, 94, 95, 96, 97.
Below: blue train 87, 86, 85, 84, 83; green train 69, 68, 64, 63, 62; red train 60, 59, 58, 57, 56.
Red numbers: 89, 87, 85, 83; 69, 67, 65, 63; 59, 57, 55, 53.
Yellow numbers: 90, 88, 86, 84; 68, 66, 64, 62; 60, 58, 56, 54.

Page 144

web, hat, cat, fox, bed, egg, sun, owl.
1. bed 2. cat 3. egg 4. fox 5. hat 6. owl 7. sun 8. web

Page 145

hook, cook, teeth, book, cheese, tree, foot, green.
moon, feet.

Pages 146-147

$4 + 7 = 11$, $8 + 5 = 13$, $6 + 9 = 15$.
+ 9 machine: $7 + 9 = 16$, $4 + 9 = 13$, $8 + 9 = 17$, $5 + 9 = 14$, $9 + 9 = 18$.
– 7 machine: $12 – 7 = 5$, $9 – 7 = 2$, $15 – 7 = 8$, $13 – 7 = 6$, $10 – 7 = 3$.
– 9 machine: $11 – 9 = 2$, $14 – 9 = 5$, $12 – 9 = 3$, $18 – 9 = 9$, $16 – 9 = 7$.

Pages 148

top: sleeping, licking.
middle: running, climbing.
bottom: swimming, flying.

Pages 149

Blue train: 8,10,12,14,16,18,20. Hidden numbers (from left to right): 3,5 8; 10,2,7; 1,9,6. Red train: 40,50, 60,70,80,90,100. Hidden numbers (from left to right): 3,6,2; 4,9,10; 8, 1.

Page 150-151

Pentagons have 5 sides. Hexagons have 6 sides. Octagons have 8 sides.

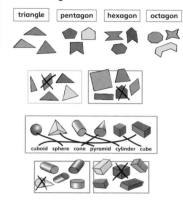

Page 152

row 1: nail, boat, coat; row 2: goat, sail, tail; row 3: snail, chain, soap, rain, toast.

Page 153

tall/ball, bees/trees, log/frog, string/swing, skate/gate, bite/kite.

Page 154-155

The difference between 3 and 7 is 4.
The difference between 5 and 11 is 6.
The difference between 6 and 10 is 4.
The difference between 7 and 12 is 5.
The difference between 9 and 4 is 5.
The difference between 6 and 11 is 5.

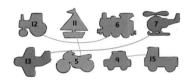

yellow submarine: 9, red submarine: 5 or 15.

Page 156

1. November. 2. January.
3. October. 4. July. 5. September.
6. May and December.

Page 157

leaf, snail, peach, seal, pail, seat. boat, mouse, coat, cloud, road.

Page 158-159

$12–9=3$, $16-5=11$, $13-8=5$, $14-7=7$, $15-6=9$, $17-9=8$, $12-8=4$, $15-9=6$, $19-9=10$, $11-9=2$. The eggs 15–6 and 14–9 are the odd ones out.
The missing numbers are: 8, 11, 9, 13; 6, 9, 11, 15; 3, 6, 14, 18.

The difference is (from left to right): 9, 9, 13; 5, 6, 4.

Page 160

bricks: ducks, chicks; king: string, ring; watch: witch, switch; whistle: castle, bottle; dress: glass, grass.

Page 161

row 1: ch, fl, sw; row 2: cr, pl, sw; row 3: fl, br, cr; row 4: br, ch, pl.

Page 162-163

$9 + 9 = 18$, $6 + 5 = 11$, pea. $12 + 8 = 20$, $11 + 7 = 18$, $8 + 3 = 11$, $7 + 7 = 14$, bean. $7 + 5 = 12$, $2 + 9 = 11$,
$10 + 7 = 17$, $8 + 9 = 17$, $9 + 6 = 15$, $10 + 9 = 19$, carrot. $8 + 8 = 16$,
$11 + 4 = 15$, $12 + 7 = 19$, $6 + 5 = 11$, $5 + 14 = 19$, $8 + 7 = 15$, potato.

The missing numbers are:
top: 10, 13, 20; middle: 4, 10, 12, 20; bottom: 7, 8, 14, 20.

Page 164

Possible answers are:
Dad is playing with a red ball.
The baby is eating a big ice-cream.
The brown dog is chasing the cat.
Mum is feeding the hungry ducks.

Page 165

starfish, waterfall, homework, playtime, toothbrush, football,
earring, bookmark.

Page 166

Mystery numbers are 11 and 15.

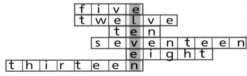

Page 167

Red fish: $7 + 0$ (= 7); yellow fish: $9 – 5$ (= 4).

Page 168

cr<u>a</u>b, dr<u>i</u>ll, dr<u>u</u>m; b<u>e</u>d, d<u>o</u>ll, t<u>e</u>nt; h<u>a</u>nd, s<u>u</u>n, z<u>i</u>p; f<u>o</u>x, b<u>u</u>s, sh<u>e</u>d; b<u>e</u>ll, c<u>a</u>p, fr<u>o</u>g.

Page 169

t<u>ee</u>th, n<u>ur</u>se, n<u>ai</u>l, l<u>ea</u>f, m<u>ou</u>se, cr<u>ow</u>n, h<u>oo</u>p, h<u>or</u>se.

Pages 170-171

5: 12 – 7, 9 – 4, 13 – 8, 11 – 6.
6: 10 – 4, 11 – 5, 9 – 3, 14 – 8.
15 – 8 = 7, 17 – 9 = 8, 14 – 6 = 8,
13 – 9 = 4, 11 – 4 = 7, 12 – 8 = 4.
The odd ones out are: top left:
18 – 9, top right: 14 – 8, centre:
17 – 9. 13 – 9 and 11 – 7, 14 – 8 and 12 – 6,
15 – 8 and 13 – 6.

Page 172

bear – pear – wear; fire – wire – hire; jaw – claw – straw; brown – clown – crown; flight – bright – knight.

Page 173

1. Kelly and Sam; 2. Sam and Anna; 3. Kelly and Anna; 4. Kelly and Anna; 5. Sam and Anna; 6. Kelly and Anna.

Page 174-175

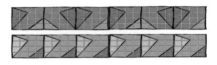

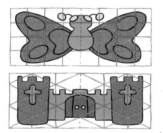

Page 176

dresses, glasses, crosses; babies, ponies, ladies, cherries.

Page 177

something = some/thing/in/tin; anyone = any/one/on/an; captain = cap/pin/pan/can.
heard = he/red/hear/ear; princess = prince/in/price/nice. You may find other words.

Pages 178-179

14 – 7 = seven, 11 – 6 = five, 13 – 7 = six, 17 – 5 = twelve, 13 – 5 = eight, 16 – 15 = one, 16 – 7 = nine. The mystery number is sixteen.
9 – 4 = 5, 8 – 7 = 1, 11 – 6 = 5, 7 – 5 = 2, 10 – 7 = 3. 12 – 6 = 6, 7 – 4 = 3, 15 – 10 = 5, 9 – 6 = 3, 11 – 4 = 7. 8 – 4 = 4, 13 – 8 = 5, 6 – 2 = 4, 10 – 5 = 5, 14 – 7 = 7. The missing numbers are: blue see-saw: 9 and 5, green see-saw: 8 and 8, yellow see-saw: 7 and 13. The missing numbers are: dog: 11, 5; pig: 17, 13, 6; hen: 18, 15, 7.

Page 180

1. Parrot said, "I like to fly and sing."
2. Monkey said, "I have a long tail."
3. Horse said, "I like to eat hay." 4. Kangaroo said, "I like to jump and hop." 5. Elephant said, "I have a long trunk."

Page 181

is not = isn't; cannot = can't;
I would = I'd; I am = I'm;
will not = won't; you have = you've.

<u>I'd</u> like to see you but <u>I'm</u> ill. I <u>can't</u> go out but <u>I'd</u> like to see you if you have time and <u>it's</u> not too far for you to come.

Page 182

Missing numbers are (from left to right): Top: 5, 1, 4; 6, 9, 3; 9, 2, 5. Middle:10, 30,70; 20, 40, 80; 20, 50, 90. Bottom: 13=10+3, 43=40+3, 62=60+2, 26=20+6, 48=40+8, 75=70+5.

Page 183

47, 74; 49, 43, 67; 44, 61, 79; 18, 27, 42.

Page 184

see, two, night, new, write.

Page 185

football, butterfly, starfish, sunglasses.

Page 186

The missing totals are (from left to right): 11, 13, 12.
The missing numbers are (from left to right): 5, 3, 7.

Page 187

Green purse: 20p; pink purse: 18p.   Box 1 : £12; box 2: £11; box 3: £16.

Page 190

thr: throne, three; str: string, straw; squ: squirrel, square.

I thr<u>ew</u> the ball in the air.

A small river is called a str<u>eam</u>.

A mouse squ<u>eaks</u>.

Page 191

Page 192

4 + 4 = 8, 6 + 6 = 12, 3 + 3 = 6, 5 + 5 = 10, 8 + 8 = 16, 2 + 2 = 4, 7 + 7 = 14, 10 + 10 = 20, 9 + 9 = 18. 3 + 4 = 7, 5 + 6 = 11, 8 + 9 =17, 10 + 9 = 19, 5 + 4 = 9, 6 + 7 = 13, 8 + 7 = 15.

Page 193

The change from 20p is: row 1: 13p, row 2: 12p, row 3: 8p, row 4: 5p.
apple – 9p change, banana – 6p change, lemon – 14p change, orange – 11p change, pear – 7p change, pineapple – 4p change.

Page 195

1. silly; 2. sensible; 3. silly; 4. silly; 5. silly; 6. sensible.

Page 196-197

6.00, 6.15, 6.30, 6.45, 7.00.

Page 198
lemon, swing, watch, horse, crane, snake.

Page 199
ch + air = chair, sn + ail = snail, sc + arf = scarf, dr + um = drum, fl + ower = flower, tr + umpet = trumpet.

Pages 200-201
The missing numbers are: top: 50, 70, 80, 90, 110; bottom: 100, 130, 140, 160, 170.
$7 + 2 = 9$, $70 + 20 = 90$; $4 + 3 = 7$, $40 + 30 = 70$; $3 + 5 = 8$, $30 + 50 = 80$; $6 + 5 = 11$, $60 + 50 = 110$.
$90 + 60 = 150$, $70 + 70 = 140$, $50 + 80 = 130$, $50 + 70 = 120$, $60 + 30 = 90$, $70 + 40 = 110$.

Pages 202
1. wet–dry; 2. soft–hard; 3. first–last; 4. far–near; 5. empty–full; 6. hot–cold; 7. night–day; 8. push–pull; 9. short–long; 10. heavy–light.

Pages 203
1. The dog barked at the burglar.
2. The horse galloped across the field. 3. The frog jumped out of the pond. 4. The birds flew into the air.
5. The spider spun a big web.
6. The cat slept on the wall.

Pages 204
Missing numbers are: 20, 25, 30, 35, 40, 45, 50. Hidden numbers are (from left to right): 1, 3, 9; 5, 6, 2; 8, 4, 7. Left: 3 fives; right: 6 fives.

Pages 205

Page 206
spoon, pea, snail, coat.

Page 208
Total of 9: $4 + 5$, $7 + 2$, $6 + 3$, $8 + 1$.
Total of 12: $4 + 8$, $5 + 7$, $6 + 6$, $9 + 3$.

Page 209
$8 + 3 = 11$, $9 - 4 = 5$, $7 + 6 = 13$, $8 + 7 = 15$, $12 - 6 = 6$, $10 - 7 = 3$, $12 - 3 = 9$, $8 + 4 = 12$.

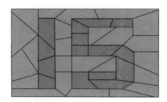

The number 15 is hidden in the picture.

Pages 210

a	e	m	c	i	g	r	t	h	j
s	r	l	c	b	t	a	l	q	k
d	o	g	s	g	r	o	w	s	z
f	k	f	m	u	e	s	b	g	s
d	g	s	t	d	e	q	n	q	u
r	u	n	l	l	f	u	d	m	p
p	x	o	l	j	y	e	u	o	n
w	c	l	o	o	v	a	l	u	t
y	a	z	e	v	n	k	y	s	b
t	h	x	a	e	c	s	w	e	d

Pages 211
or, let, is, as, pea, at, mat, me.
man/pan; coat/boat; robber/rubber; card/cart; fork/fort; wolf/golf.

Pages 212
top row: 3 balls; middle row: 3 balls; bottom row: 2 balls.

Pages 213
parrots: 2 twos and 3 twos;
ducks: 3 threes and 4 threes;
marbles: 3 fours, 2 fours and 4 fours.

Page 214
would/wood, meet/meat, hair/hare, me/tea, bed/head, maid/made, sigh/fly, plane/train.

Pages 216-217
The missing numbers are: top: 110, 90, 80, 50; middle: 130, 100, 90, 80; bottom: 170, 150, 120, 80. $8 - 3 = 5$, $80 - 30 = 50$; $7 - 4 = 3$, $70 - 40 = 30$, $15 - 8 = 7$, $150 - 80 = 70$; $9 - 5 = 4$, $90 - 50 = 40$, $12 - 7 = 5$, $120 - 70 = 50$; $14 - 6 = 8$, $140 - 60 = 80$.

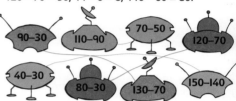

110 and 60, 40 and 90, 130 and 80, 170 and 120.

Pages 218
1. May; 2. shape; 3. paint; 4. lion; 5. man. Shapes = square, triangle, circle, rectangle. Farm animals = sheep, horse, pig, cow. Vehicles = bus, car, lorry ,van. Days of week = Monday, Friday, Tuesday, Sunday.
Colours = red, orange, blue, green.

Pages 219

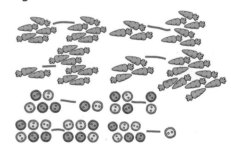

Pages 220
cl – clown, dr – drum, sn – snail, bl – blue, gr – grapes, sp – spider, st – star, sw – swan.

Page 221

The missing letters are:
c f.
<u>d</u>ragon, <u>c</u>lown, <u>s</u>poon.

Page 222

Missing numbers (from left to right):
3, 3, 6, 9; 5, 4, 4, 12; 3, 6, 0, 10; 8, 3, 8, 9.
Odd numbers to be coloured are: 13, 33,
49, 65, 81, 85. Shape names are:
triangle, pentagon, hexagon, cone,
cylinder, pyramid.

Page 223

is not = isn't; I would = I'd;
cannot = can't. Nouns: dog, mouse, tree.
Verbs: grows, run, squeaks.
Adjectives = tall, soft, cold.

Page 224

cl, br, cr, bl;
dr, gr, pl, fl.

spider→spade
snake→snail
swan→swing
star→stool

Page 225

1. ship, 2. sheep, 3. shell.
cows, farmers, cats.

Page 226

two–2, six–6, three–3, eight–8, ten–10,
four–4, seven–7, nine–9, one–1, five–5.
 er ce ake ar tch ing

Page 227

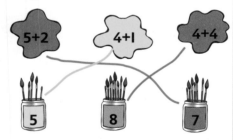

5 balls take away 3 balls = 2 balls,
4 balls take away 3 balls = 1 ball.

Page 228

9 sweets altogether, 6 cakes altogether.
6 and 2 make 8 altogether. 8 take away
2 leaves 6, 4 take away 2 leaves 2.

Page 229

wall/bell, sock/clock, ring/swing.
hook, cook, teeth.

Page 230

Blue train: 8,10,12,14,16,18,20.
Hidden numbers (from left to right):
3,5 8; 10,2,7; 1,9,6. Red train: 40,50,
60,70,80,90,100. Hidden numbers
(from left to right): 3,6,2; 4,9,10; 8, 1.

Page 231

$5 + 5 = 10$. $6 - 4 = 2$, $10 - 4 = 6$.

Page 232

glasses, dresses, babies, ponies.
horse, swing, watch.